Editor
Lorin Klistoff, M.A.

Managing Editor
Karen J. Goldfluss, M.S. Ed.

Editor-in-Chief
Sharon Coan, M.S. Ed.

Cover Artist
Lesley Palmer

Art Coordinator
Denice Adorno

Imaging
Rosa C. See

Product Manager
Phil Garcia

Publishers
Rachelle Cracchiolo, M.S. Ed.
Mary Dupuy Smith, M.S. Ed.

Daily Skills Practice

Grades 4-5

Author

Jane Hutchison

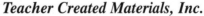

Teacher Created Materials, Inc.
6421 Industry Way
Westminster, CA 92683
www.teachercreated.com

©2001 Teacher Created Materials, Inc.
Made in U.S.A.
ISBN-0-7439-3302-8

Table of Contents

Introduction

Daily Skills Practice: Grades 4–5 was designed to cover a wide range of skills and concepts typically introduced or reviewed during a school year. The practice pages provide a quick assessment of how a child is performing on a particular skill or with a specific concept. In addition, the activities in this book provide teachers, children, and parents with consistent, daily feedback on a child's academic progress.

How to Use the Practice Pages

In the Classroom

The daily skills pages are easily implemented in the classroom during whole-class instruction. Here are some suggestions for introducing and assigning the pages:

- To use some or all of the practice sheets for whole-class or group instruction, simply photocopy them onto overhead transparency sheets and use them throughout the year. Students will need to have a daily practice notebook to copy the exercises off the overhead. This is an excellent way to begin each morning, by having their practice sheet on an overhead ready for students when they walk into the room. The transparencies can be organized and stored for use for many years.

- Give each child a photocopy of the daily practice sheet you wish to use or prepare a small packet for each child. Send the packets home every one to two weeks. Decide how you will review and assess the children's completed work and communicate this to both the children and the parents.

At Home

The practice pages in this book make excellent reinforcement exercises at home. With over 200 daily practice pages from which to choose, a child is given the opportunity to review concepts and skills he or she already knows. For newly acquired skills, the pages provide reinforcement through practice. As pages are completed, parents and children can work together to correct the exercises using the answer key provided in the back of the book.

Practice Page Sections

Each practice page is divided into the following sections:

- **Math Practice**—Math Practice consists of a variety of math problems. Generally, there is a word problem at the end of each math section.

- **Language Practice**—Language Practice consists of a variety of grammar and writing skills. This is an effective way to quickly preview or review a skill.

- **Writing Practice**—Each day, a writing prompt is given for students to practice their writing skills. Students should be encouraged to write at least a paragraph of 5–6 sentences. Give students reading practice by letting them share their writings with the class.

See the Table of Contents for a list of specific skills and page numbers used in these sections.

(**Note:** If you wish to extend the activities by writing your own lessons, reproduce the blank skills practice form provided on page 206.)

Name _____

Math Practice: Addition and Subtraction

For problems 1–4, write each problem in words and solve. Then solve problem 5.

1. $\begin{array}{r} 27 \\ +\ 46 \\ \hline \end{array}$	2. $\begin{array}{r} 106 \\ -\ 85 \\ \hline \end{array}$	3. $\begin{array}{r} 99 \\ +\ 23 \\ \hline \end{array}$
_____ _____ _____	_____ _____ _____	_____ _____ _____

4. $\begin{array}{r} 243 \\ -\ 19 \\ \hline \end{array}$ _____ _____ _____	5. Jason collected books. He had 13 mysteries, 5 insect books, 7 joke books, and 21 picture books. How many books did he have in all? _____

Language Practice: Subject

Underline the subject in each sentence.

1. The children ate pizza for lunch.

2. June and Susan traveled to Florida.

3. The boy and his dog played with the ball.

4. Good stories are found in books.

5. The little girl talked to the clown.

 Writing Practice: Write a paragraph about how you feel beginning this new school year. Include things you would like to do this year.

Math Practice: Place Value

Look at the number **3,458**. Answer the questions about place value. Then solve number 5.

1. What place is the 5 in?	2. What place is the 3 in?	3. What place is the 4 in?
3,458	**3,458**	**3,458**
_____	_____	_____

4. What is the number value of the 5?	5. Joe had 32 marbles and gave Anita and Kim 8 each. How many did he have for himself?
3,458	
_____	_____

Language Practice: Predicate

Underline the predicate in each sentence.

1. The baseball team played on Saturday.

2. The students sang songs in choir.

3. Stars flicker and sparkle in the sky.

4. My favorite food is tacos.

5. Kim had to stay after school to finish her class work.

 Writing Practice: Write a paragraph with the following beginning phrase.

People like me because . . .

Math Practice: Patterns

Complete the pattern.

1. 10, 20, 30, ___, ___, ___, ___, ___, ___, ___, ___, ___, ___, ___, ___, ___	2. 15, 25, 35, ___, ___, ___, ___, ___, ___, ___, ___, ___, ___, ___, ___, ___	3. 20, 25, 30, ___, ___, ___, ___, ___, ___, ___, ___, ___, ___, ___, ___, ___
4. 25, 50, 75, ___, ___, ___, ___, ___, ___, ___, ___, ___, ___, ___, ___, ___	5. You have 4 dollars, 1 quarter, 3 dimes, 3 nickels, and 4 pennies. How much money do you have in all? _____	

Language Practice: Sentences

Circle the correct phrase to complete the sentences.

1. The girl at school (her homework, yesterday, completed her work).

2. Animals at the zoo (with each other, eat and play together, morning).

3. (Travel in pairs, Birds, At Night) fly in the sky.

4. (The students, Hopefully, Finally) turned in their library books late.

5. Our class (played outside, outside, homework).

Writing Practice: Write a short story for this title.

Help! I'm Being Chased by a Tiger!

Math Practice: Reading a Graph

Use the graph to answer the following questions.

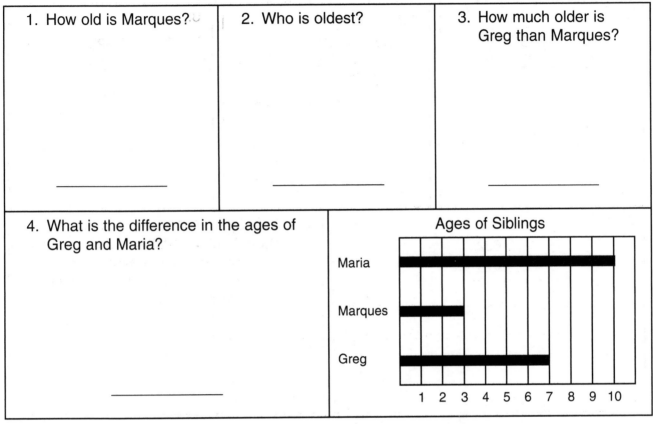

1. How old is Marques?	2. Who is oldest?	3. How much older is Greg than Marques?

4. What is the difference in the ages of Greg and Maria?

Ages of Siblings

Maria

Marques

Greg

1 2 3 4 5 6 7 8 9 10

Language Practice: Possessive Nouns

Write the possessive form of each singular noun. Then write a sentence with each one.

Possessive   **Sentence**

1. boy _____ _____

2. Susan _____ _____

3. dog _____ _____

4. sky _____ _____

5. teacher _____ _____

6. mom _____ _____

 Writing Practice: Write a descriptive paragraph about the month of September. Include things you like or dislike.

Math Practice: Mixed Computation

Solve the problems below.

1.
 	
   243
 + 76
	2.
	
	   500
	 − 23
		3.
		
		   325
		 x 4

4.
 	
   632
 + 378
	5. Mrs. Spadafino drives 20 miles to school. Mrs. Hutchison drives 13 miles, Mrs. Martin drives 8 miles, and Mrs. Olive drives 6 miles. How many total miles do they drive?
	
	   _____	

Language Practice: Kinds of Sentences

Write the correct letter beside each sentence.

_____ 1. Pass the butter, please.   D. Declarative

_____ 2. There was a shooting star out last night.   E. Exclamatory

_____ 3. What a beautiful sunrise this morning!   I. Imperative

_____ 4. Did you see a movie on Saturday?   Q. Interrogative

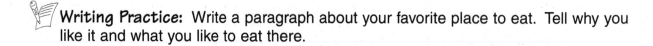 **Writing Practice:** Write a paragraph about your favorite place to eat. Tell why you like it and what you like to eat there.

Name _____

Math Practice: Rounding

Round to the nearest 10. Then solve problem 5.

1. 42 _____	2. 78 _____	3. 55 _____

4. 186 _____

5. Daniel saw 16 trees, 12 bushes, 23 flowers, and 2 lizards on his walk in the woods. How many items did Daniel see? _____

Language Practice: Compound Words

Find these compound words in the puzzle.

backyard

lipstick

somebody

bookmark

mailbox

toothbrush

friendship

sailboat

f	k	m	c	g	f	z	r	s	t
d	r	a	y	k	c	a	b	o	a
m	a	i	l	b	o	x	o	m	o
t	m	l	e	c	t	t	i	e	b
n	k	z	i	n	h	d	n	b	l
i	o	t	r	b	d	s	k	o	i
s	o	u	r	x	g	s	h	d	a
g	b	u	c	i	v	s	h	y	s
h	s	r	g	c	k	s	k	i	p
h	k	c	i	t	s	p	i	l	p

Writing Practice: Practice your letter writing skills. Write a letter to your teacher.

Math Practice: Standard Form

Write each in standard form for problems 1–4. Then solve problem 5.

1. 52 thousand 3 hundred _____	2. 4 thousand twenty-three _____	3. 1 hundred five _____
4. 4 hundred ninety-nine _____	5. There were 16 people in the gym, and seven were girls. How many were boys? _____	

Language Practice: Plurals

Write the plural of these nouns.

1. goose _____   4. city _____   7. cherry _____

2. ox _____   5. book _____   8. class _____

3. sheep _____   6. leaf _____

Now choose four plurals and write them in a complete sentence.

_____

_____

_____

_____

✏️ **Writing Practice:** Write a descriptive paragraph by finishing the story.

I was walking down the street when suddenly I saw a bright light.

Math Practice: Estimation

Estimate by rounding, then write your estimated sum or difference. Then solve problem 5.

1. Round to the nearest hundred. 123 $+\ 456$	2. Round to the nearest hundred. 798 $-\ 144$	3. Round to the nearest thousand. $6{,}198$ $+\ 2{,}781$
4. Round to the nearest thousand. $5{,}110$ $-\ 1{,}529$	5. If Caleb read 12 pages on Monday, 56 pages on Tuesday, and 9 pages on Wednesday, how many pages did he read in all? _____	

Language Practice: Adverbs

Fill in the blank with the correct adverb.

1. He walked _____ to the car.

2. We have to get up early _____.

3. The team _____ ran around the field.

4. My sister sings _____.

5. His friend is _____ considerate of others.

tomorrow
beautifully
slowly
quickly
very

Writing Practice: You've won a contest and you are on your way to the moon. Write a paragraph about your adventures.

Math Practice: Standard Form

For problems 1–4, write in standard form. The solve problem 5.

1. 7 tens 4 ones _____	2. 90 + 5 = _____	3. thirty-six _____
4. 400 + 70 + 1 = _____	5. What number is 2 less than ten thousand, one? _____	

Language Practice: Compound Words

Connect the two words to make a compound word.

rain	ground
back	writer
grass	fly
base	forest
type	mother
grand	boat
star	ball
cup	fish
butter	hopper
sail	cake

Writing Practice: Write a paragraph about what Labor Day means.

Math Practice: Rounding

Round to the nearest 100. Then solve problem 5.

1. 864	2. 729	3. 671
_____	_____	_____

4. 5,329	5. Greta is 6 years younger than her brother. Her brother is 13. How old is Greta?
_____	_____

Language Practice: Contractions

Circle the correct contraction for each sentence.

1. We (won't, willn't) arrive at school late.

2. The food (wasn't, was'nt) cooked properly.

3. They (hav'nt, haven't) done their chores this week.

4. (I'ave, I've) seen a meteor fall from the sky.

5. It looks like (it's, its') going to rain.

Writing Practice: Write about your favorite foods. What are they, and why do you like them? Then draw a picture of them.

Math Practice: Place Value

For problems 1–2, write the numeral in word form. For problems 3–4, write the numbers in the boxes. Then solve problem 5.

1. 305 _____ _____ _____	2. 2,295 _____ _____ _____	3. two hundred six

4. eight thousand, one hundred forty-four	5. Mrs. Green and Ms. Ward bought school supplies for $13.42. If they paid with $20.00, what would their change be? _____

Language Practice: Pronouns

Circle all pronouns in each sentence.

1. They asked if their teacher could give them some help.

2. The dog ate her hot dog after she dropped it on the floor.

3. Shoes were found in my locker, and they weren't mine.

4. My family likes to go shopping with our cousin.

5. We weren't sure if the present belonged to her.

 Writing Practice: Write a paragraph about the best birthday party you ever had.

Math Practice: Number Sentences

Write a number sentence for each word problem. Then solve.

1. The judges ordered 28 ribbons and 32 trophies for the contest. How many prizes were ordered? _____	2. A circus has 7 clowns, 3 monkeys, and 6 tigers. How many are in the circus in all? _____	3. Joy baked 12 cookies. She gave 7 cookies to a friend. How many cookies are left for her? _____
4. Todd has 8 stamps. On Friday his brother bought 15. How many more stamps does Todd's brother have? _____		5. Kenya had 3 basketballs, 2 footballs, 1 soccer ball, and 5 baseballs. How many balls did he have in all? _____

Language Practice: Common and Proper Nouns

Write **C** for *common* and **P** for *proper* nouns.

_____ 1. house

_____ 2. White House

_____ 3. Jill

_____ 4. sister

_____ 5. state

_____ 6. Missouri

_____ 7. toy store

_____ 8. store

_____ 9. deer

_____ 10. Deerfield St.

 Writing Practice: Write a paragraph explaining what it means when someone says "beauty is only skin deep." Then tell about someone you think is beautiful inside.

Name _____

Math Practice: Subtraction with Money

Solve each problem.

1.	2.	3.
$0.96 − $0.34	$1.09 − $0.21	$7.42 − $6.71

4.	5. Sharon bought a piece of candy for 14 cents. If she gave the cashier $1.00, what five coins would she get back? Draw and label each coin.
$4.50 − $3.28	

Language Practice: Story Comprehension and Following Directions

Read the story about insects. From the description, draw an insect and label each part.

Insects An insect is a six-legged invertebrate. It has 3 oval-shaped parts that connect to each other. The first part is a head. Then it has a thorax, and last it has an abdomen. Insects also have eyes and a pair of antennas.	*(drawing)*

 Writing Practice: Finish this statement with a descriptive paragraph.

This weekend I . . .

Math Practice: Column Addition

Solve each problem.

1.	2.	3.
33 54 18 + 25	42 10 26 + 13	72 6 12 + 30

4.	5. Michael had 18 books. He gave Erika 3 books and Shemika twice as many as he gave Erika. How many books did Michael have left?
61 16 56 + 15	_____

Language Practice: Alphabetical Order

Write the names of these famous Americans in alphabetical order by last name.

Captain John Smith   _____

Pocahontas   _____

Miles Standish   _____

John Paul Jones   _____

Paul Revere   _____

George Washington   _____

James Madison   _____

Benjamin Franklin   _____

John Adams   _____

John Quincy Adams   _____

 Writing Practice: September 16 is National Student Day. Write how you would like to see the students at your school honored.

Math Practice: Reading a Graph

Use the pictograph to answer the questions.

1. Which student was tardy the most?	2. Which student was tardy 3 days?	3. How many times was Joe tardy?
_____	_____	_____

4. If each ✻ meant 2 days of being tardy, how many days would Beth have been tardy?

_____

Students With Tardies

Sue	✻ ✻ ✻
Tamika	✻
Joe	✻ ✻
Jamal	✻ ✻ ✻ ✻ ✻
Beth	✻ ✻

✻ = 1 tardy

Language Practice: Subject and Predicate

Read each sentence. Decide how the underlined words are used.

_____ 1. The <u>football team</u> played a game yesterday.

_____ 2. The rabbits <u>hopped and jumped</u> in the grass.

_____ 3. Sunshine <u>is</u> very warm on your face.

_____ 4. <u>Donna and Jane</u> are best friends.

A. Simple Subject

B. Simple Predicate

C. Compound Subject

D. Compound Predicate

 Writing Practice: August is National Invention Month. Describe something you would like to invent and then draw a picture of it.

Math Practice: Reading a Graph

Use the bar graph to answer the questions.

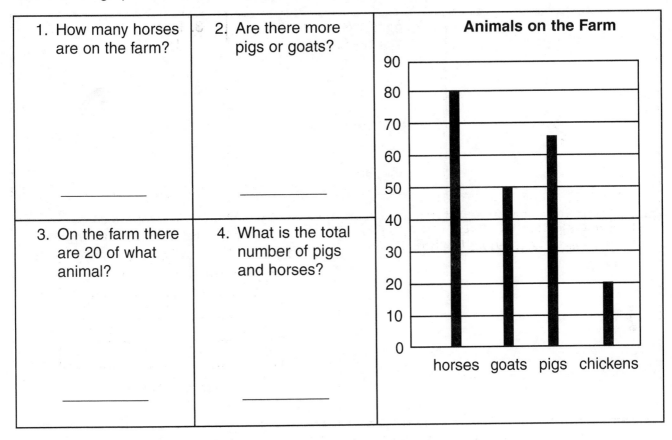

1. How many horses are on the farm?	2. Are there more pigs or goats?
_____	_____
3. On the farm there are 20 of what animal?	4. What is the total number of pigs and horses?
_____	_____

Animals on the Farm

horses goats pigs chickens

Language Practice: Possessive Nouns

Add an **'s** or **'** to each word to show ownership.

1. The child _____ toy was put on the shelf.

2. Please turn your papers in the teacher _____ box.

3. Bobby found his friends _____ baseball cards outside.

4. Mrs. Saxton _____ students went on a field trip.

5. The dog _____ bone was buried under the tree.

 Writing Practice: Write a paragraph describing a time you went to a fair. Include your favorite ride and all the things you saw.

Math Practice: Place Value

For problems 1–4, find what number value is represented by the **7**. Then solve problem 5.

1. 76 _____	2. 927 _____	3. 7,253 _____
4. 6,745 _____	5. Sherwon had 38 baseball cards. He gave 10 to Antwone. How many cards does Sherwon have left? _____	

Language Practice: Sentence Fragments

Finish each fragment to make complete sentences.

1. Jose came to_____.

2. Watch out for_____.

3. _____ finished the race.

4. _____ comes down the road.

5. An ugly bug_____.

6. _____ is pink with green stripes.

 Writing Practice: During holidays students get some extra days off from school. Write a paragraph about things you will do on your days off from school.

Name _____

Math Practice: Place Value

For problems 1–2, write the numbers in the boxes. For problems 3–4, write the numeral in word form. Then solve problem 5.

1. fifteen thousand, seventy-two	2. three hundred thirty thousand, one hundred two	3. 888

4. 4,236

5. Using the number of boys and girls in your class, write a number sentence showing how many students are in your class.

Language Practice: Sentences

Rewrite the paragraph with complete sentences. Remember to add correct end marks and capital letters.

During school today we had a test the test was in social studies we had to write the capital of each state I got two answers wrong the capital of Missouri is Springfield, not St. Louis, the capital of California is Sacramento, not Los Angeles.

Writing Practice: Pretend you are a meteorologist for a television station. Write a weather forecast for the news by how it looks outside today.

Math Practice: Addition and Subtraction with Money

Solve the problems.

1. $4.87 + $1.87	2. $10.23 + $ 7.64	3. $6.20 − $1.11
4. $8.23 − $2.50	5. Mrs. Mayberry bought pencils for $3.18, and Mrs. Penn bought notebooks for $8.76. How much money did they spend in all? _____	

Language Practice: Sentence or Fragment

Read each group of words. Then write an **S** if it is a sentence, or write an **F** if it is a fragment.

_____ 1. Wrote my homework down.

_____ 2. She is a good friend.

_____ 3. Mrs. Green a nice teacher.

_____ 4. Sit down and do your work quietly.

_____ 5. Hey, being in the fourth grade is going to be fun!

 Writing Practice: You just earned $50.00. Write a story about how you earned the money and what you would buy with $50.00.

Math Practice: Logic

Read each statement and write the results.

1. Jerry is taller than Jamal. Shemeka is taller than Jerry. And Ollie is shorter than Jamal. Write in order the tallest to the shortest student. _____ _____	2. Ben sits by Joan. Kim sits by a girl, and Theron sits beside Kim. Write the order in which students are sitting next to each other. _____ _____	3. Eric runs the race faster than Loren. Bob wins the race. Mara finishes in front of Eric. Write in order first through fourth place. _____ _____
4. Emily jumped higher than Sharon. Karen jumped higher than Emily. Sara did not jump as high as Sharon. Write in order the highest to lowest jumper. _____ _____	5. Leo ate less pizza than Julio. Tyrone ate less pizza than Leo. James ate the most pizza. Write in order who ate the most pizza to who ate the least. _____ _____	

Language Practice: Alphabetical Order

Write the names of these presidents in alphabetical order.

George Washington _____

Abraham Lincoln _____

John Adams _____

William Harrison _____

Dwight Eisenhower _____

Ronald Reagan _____

Jimmy Carter _____

Gerald Ford _____

Richard Nixon _____

Bill Clinton _____

 Writing Practice: If you could visit any continent, which one would it be, and why? Write a paragraph about your adventures.

Math Practice: Place Value

Fill in the blanks. Then solve problem 5.

1. In the number 3,745, the digit in the hundreds place is _____.	2. In the number 3,745, the digit in the thousands place is _____.	3. In the number 583,564, the number value of the 8 is _____.
4. In the number 583,564, the number value of the 6 is _____.	5. Sherrie had 12 pairs of earrings. Her sister borrowed 3 pairs. How many pairs of earrings did she have left? _____	

Language Practice: Nouns

Circle all nouns in the following paragraph.

Thanksgiving

Thanksgiving is an American holiday. It is observed on the fourth Thursday in November. It all began many years ago when the Indians helped the Pilgrims who had come to America. The Indians helped them plant crops and showed them how to survive in their new land. They celebrated by eating a feast together. This is how Thanksgiving began.

Writing Practice: Write a paragraph using the starting sentence below.

If I were an animal, I would be . . .

Math Practice: Addition and Subtraction

Solve the problems.

1.	2.	3.
472 + 29	482 + 19	921 – 19

4.	5. Tonya bought a cheeseburger for $1.50, French fries for $0.50, and a soda for $0.50.
839 – 228	How much did she pay for her meal? _____ How much change would she get back if she paid with a $5.00 bill? _____

Language Practice: Adjectives

Write an adjective in each blank.

1. A _____ girl walked down the street.

2. Mom bought us _____ pads of paper.

3. The _____ car had a flat tire.

4. The children built a _____ snowman.

5. The _____ grapes tasted sweet.

Writing Practice: Which sport do you like to play? Write a persuasive paragraph telling why your sport is the best.

Math Practice: Mixed Computation

Solve each problem.

1.	2.	3.
37,777 + 25,666	6,001 − 2,594	67 x 49

4.	5. Mrs. Lewis' class is going on a field trip. There are 20 students going, and 4 children can ride in each car. How many cars will be needed?
8)‾96‾	_____

Language Practice: Possessive Nouns

Circle the group of words with the correct possessive form.

1. A. the girls doll
   B. the girl's doll
   C. the girls's doll

2. A. Maria's desk
   B. Marias' desk
   C. Marias desk

3. A. my moms car
   B. my mom's car
   C. my moms's car

4. A. the children's pets
   B. the childrens pets
   C. the childrens' pets

Writing Practice: Write a scary story beginning with the phrase below.

I could not believe my eyes . . .

Math Practice: Expanded/Standard Form

For problems 1–2, write the standard form in expanded form. For problems 3–4, write the expanded form into standard form. Then solve problem 5.

1.	2.	3.
492 = ____ + ____ + ____	1,021 = ____ + ____ + ____ + ____	1,000 + 900 + 2 = _____

4.	5. Laurie earned $25.68 for helping clean the garage. Lewis earned $2.45 more than Laurie for also washing the car. How much money did Lewis earn?
20,000 + 8,000 + 300 + 10 + 9 = _____	_____

Language Practice: Abbreviations

Connect the titles of these names with the correct abbreviation.

Doctor	Jr.
Senator	Gov.
Governor	Dr.
Mister	Rev.
Reverend	Mr.
Junior	Sen.

Writing Practice: Finish the sentence below. Then write a detailed description of how your costume would look. Then draw a picture of you in your costume.

On Halloween, I want to be a . . .

Math Practice: Equivalent Numbers

For problems 1–4, write <, >, or = in the circle. Then solve problem 5.

1.

43 (<) 63

2.

260 (>) 206

3.

251 (>) 215

4.

110 (>) 101

5. Kayla brought 10 cookies for lunch. She shared 3 each with Shannon and Alyieh. How many cookies did Kayla end up eating?

_____

Language Practice: Abbreviations

Match these street names with the correct abbreviation.

Avenue	Blvd.
Street	Cir.
Boulevard	Ave.
Drive	Hwy.
Circle	Dr.
Highway	St.

Writing Practice: Finish the sentence below and then write a paragraph telling what you really enjoy doing.

What I really enjoy doing is . . .

Math Practice: Rounding

Round to the nearest hundred. Then solve problem 5.

1. 123 _____	2. 789 _____	3. 2,713 _____
4. 22,503 _____	5. Count the number of students in your classroom. Add 10 to the total. Then multiply by 2. Subtract the number of students in your room. What number did you end up with? _____ What would you have to do next to get the number you started with? _____ _____	

Language Practice: Plurals

Circle the correct plural form.

1. woman
   (womans, women, womens)

2. child
   (childs, child's, children)

3. box
   (boxes, boxs, box's)

4. deer
   (deers, deer's, deer)

5. city
   (citys, cities, cityes)

6. brush
   (brushs, brushes, brushses)

 Writing Practice: Explain in a paragraph why you would or would not like to get married someday.

Math Practice: Multiplication

Solve each problem.

1. 4 x 10 = _____	2. 2 x 12 = _____	3. 3 x 11 = _____
4. 5 x 12 = _____	5. After trick-or-treating, Stephen counted his goodies. He had 12 chocolate bars, 8 pieces of bubble gum, 6 suckers, 9 fruit chews, 10 pieces of hard candy, and 5 apples. How many goodies did he get in all? _____	

Language Practice: Contractions

Circle the correct contraction.

1. you are   (you're, your're)

2. should not   (should'nt, shouldn't)

3. we are   (wea're, we're)

4. would not   (wouldn't, would'nt)

5. he is   (his, he's)

6. they will   (they'll, they'ill)

7. will not   (willn't, won't)

8. she had   (she'ad, she'd)

9. I am   (I'm, Iam)

10. they are   (they're, theyre)

 Writing Practice: Write a paragraph telling ways to be safe while trick-or-treating.

Math Practice: Subtraction with Money

Solve each problem.

1. $\quad\quad$ $20.00 $-$ $ 2.43	**2.** $\quad\quad$ $6.02 $-$ $3.45	**3.** $\quad\quad$ $3.94 $-$ $3.08

4. $\quad\quad$ $70.00 $-$ $29.95	**5.** If you bought snacks that totaled $6.89, how much change would you get if you paid with $10.00? $\quad\quad$ _____

Language Practice: Plurals

Write the plural of the nouns below. Then write a sentence containing the plural word.

1. boy   (_____) _____

2. dish   (_____) _____

3. song (_____) _____

4. fox   (_____) _____

5. knife (_____) _____

6. ship   (_____) _____

 Writing Practice: Write a paragraph about fun things you can do outside during the fall season. Then circle all plural words.

Math Practice: Reading a Table

Use the table to answer the questions.

1. How many more pencils does Charles have than Kim? _____	2. Who has more pencils, Rachel or Kim? _____	3. How many pencils does Taryn need in order to have the same amount as Phillippe? _____

4. How many pencils are there in all?

_____

Student	Amount of Pencils
Kim	3
Charles	12
Rachel	7
Taryn	1
Phillippe	5

Language Practice: Punctuation

Add quotation marks where they belong.

1. We sang The Star Spangled Banner at the baseball game.

2. My mom read the poem The Raven to me.

3. Our family saw The Pearls of Parlay, a short story, at the theater.

4. The band aboard the ship played Nearer My God to Thee.

5. The newspaper printed an article entitled 2000: The Millennium.

 Writing Practice: Peace, Friendship, and Good Will Week is in October. Write a paragraph about what you think will make all of these things happen in your classroom. Then underline which ones you will work on.

Math Practice: Multiplication

Multiply.

1. 3 x 3 = _____	2. 5 x 5 = _____	3. 7 x 7 = _____

4.

11 x 11 = _____

5. Write one of the number sentences above into a word problem.

_____

_____

_____

_____

Language Practice: Abbreviations

Find the abbreviations to each month in the puzzle.

January										
February	E	F	G	O	C	T	H	Z	R	R
March	H	U	T	Y	H	J	K	R	P	J
April	A	N	L	R	A	R	J	R	A	T
August	P	G	I	N	A	O	A	K	Y	Y
September	J	F	A	P	C	I	C	M	O	W
October	S	E	H	V	X	X	Z	M	Y	C
November	E	B	X	F	N	V	Z	D	S	G
December	P	W	K	Y	H	O	B	E	H	E
	T	E	X	J	H	C	V	C	N	S
	B	Q	R	F	X	I	J	E	Z	I

 Writing Practice: Columbus Day is in the month of October. Write a short story about traveling on a ship across the ocean.

Name _____

Math Practice: Multiplication

Solve each problem.

1. 438 x 4	2. 312 x 5	3. 2,263 x 8
4. 3,259 x 4	5. The Titans scored 3 touchdowns and 1 field goal when they played the Cowboys. The Cowboys scored 2 touchdowns and 3 field goals. What was the score? (**Hint:** touchdown = 7 points [with extra point], field goal = 3 points) Titans _____ Cowboys _____ Who won? _____	

Language Practice: Punctuation

Underline or add quotation marks for each title.

1. Charlotte's Web (a book)

2. Beauty and the Beast (a movie)

3. Expanding the West (a chapter in a book)

4. Titanic (a ship)

5. People (a magazine)

6. How to Make a Cake (an article)

7. The Boston Globe (a newspaper)

8. West Side Story (a play)

 Writing Practice: Write a paragraph describing what you think a Titan is. Then draw a picture of a Titan.

Math Practice: Equivalent Fractions

Fill in the missing number and then solve problem 5.

1. $\dfrac{3}{12} = \dfrac{}{4}$	2. $\dfrac{2}{3} = \dfrac{}{9}$	3. $\dfrac{1}{2} = \dfrac{}{16}$

4. $\dfrac{4}{16} = \dfrac{}{4}$	5. Justin's word in a word game made 12 points, but then it was doubled. Quentin's word made 20 points, but then it was tripled. What is Justin's and Quentin's score now? Justin's score = _____ Quentin's score = _____

Language Practice: Common/Proper Nouns

Fill in the blanks with nouns.

Common	Proper
city	_____
_____	Tennessee
river	_____
_____	Jupiter
boy	_____
_____	Dr. Simpson

 Writing Practice: Write a short story about living in the Mohave Desert. Circle each common noun and underline each proper noun.

Name _____

Math Practice: Division

Divide and then solve problem 5.

1. 28 ÷ 7 = _____	2. 64 ÷ 8 = _____	3. 72 ÷ 9 = _____
4. 42 ÷ 6 = _____	5. Juanita wanted to divide the cookies she made between her and her 3 friends. She made 2 dozen cookies. How many cookies did each girl get? _____	

Language Practice: Adverbs

Unscramble these adverbs.

1. stfa _____

2. ryelal _____

3. nyoilis _____

4. yadot _____

5. dably _____

6. lelw _____

7. vyer _____

8. lyetuiq _____

 Writing Practice: Write a persuasive paragraph telling someone why the state you live in is the best state there is.

Math Practice: Multiplication

Solve each problem.

1. 42 x 8	**2.** 124 x 3	**3.** 235 x 4
4. 2,346 x 2	**5.** Kym watched television for 2 hours on Friday, 3 hours on Saturday, and on Sunday twice as much as on Friday. How many hours did she watch over the three days? _____	

Language Practice: Nouns

Write these nouns under the correct heading.

Spain
tears
girl
book
Houston
love
student
cat
desk
cousin
state
happiness

Person	Place	Thing	Idea

 Writing Practice: September is "All-American Breakfast Month." Write a paragraph about your favorite breakfast.

Name _____

Math Practice: Decimals and Fractions

For problems 1–2, write each fraction as a decimal. For problems 3–4, write each decimal as a fraction. Then solve problem 5.

1. $\frac{6}{10} =$ _____	2. $\frac{4}{10} =$ _____	3. $.7 =$ _____

4. $.2 =$ _____	5. The Watsons had a pizza for supper. It was divided into 8 slices. Joey, his mom, and his dad each had $\frac{1}{4}$ of the pizza. How many slices did each person eat? _____

Language Practice: Alphabetical Order

Write these words in alphabetical order.

penny   _____

person   _____

pansy   _____

particular   _____

period   _____

ponder   _____

pick   _____

Writing Practice: You have been chosen to make a speech at school about recycling. Write what you would say in your speech. Be sure to include the reasons why we should recycle.

Math Practice: Even/Odd

Write *even* or *odd* below each number. Then solve problem 5.

1. 24	2. 520	3. 83
_____	_____	_____

4. 395	5. Farmer Brown has 382 cows. 128 of them are brown. How many of his cows are not brown?
_____	_____

Language Practice: Commas

Place commas where needed.

1. He ran jumped and skipped down the street.

2. Betty bought a notebook a pen a pencil and a pack of paper for school.

3. We drove down the street beside the fire station and across the parkway to the video store.

4. My teacher gave me spelling history and geometry for homework.

5. When I get home from school, I eat a snack do my homework eat supper and go to bed.

Writing Practice: Write a paragraph using the sentence starter below.

If I was rich, I would . . .

Name _____

Math Practice: Place Value

Look at the number **976,423** and answer the questions. Then solve problem 5.

1. What is the place value of 4? **976,423** _____	2. What is the place value of 3? **976,423** _____	3. What is the number value of 6? **976,423** _____
4. What is the number value of 2? **976,423** _____	5. Frankie talked on the phone for 20 minutes. Jerry talked on the phone for $\frac{1}{2}$ of the time. How many minutes did Jerry talk on the phone? _____	

Language Practice: Commas

Write a **C** for correct or a **N** for not correct beside each sentence.

_____ 1. Lindsay turn off your, CD player.

_____ 2. "I like to play my video games," said Patrick.

_____ 3. How old are you, Laura?

_____ 4. Robert lives in Knoxville Tennessee.

_____ 5. Joey said "Kevin you are a good bowler."

_____ 6. Kimberly's cousins are Megan, Christen, and Katie.

_____ 7. "Before we eat, Stephen, you need to set the table," said Jenny.

_____ 8. Stephanie have you helped your sister Suzanne?

Writing Practice: Finish the statement below and write a paragraph on what makes you happy.

Happiness is . . .

Math Practice: Addition and Subtraction

Solve the problems. Be careful to follow the signs.

1. 346 $+\ 421$	2. 259 $+\ 630$	3. 987 $-\ 183$
4. 906 $-\ 412$	5. One shark ate 64 fish. Another shark ate 21 fish. How many fish were eaten in all? _____	

Language Practice: Pronouns

Fill in the blanks with the correct pronoun. Capitalize when necessary.

it	my	our	her	we	I	they

1. _____ sister, Ana, and _____ friend went to the mall.

2. _____ shopped for two hours.

3. Ana and _____ went back the next day.

4. _____ bought _____ mother a birthday present.

5. Mom said she liked _____ very much.

Writing Practice: Finish the statement below and write a paragraph about your adventures. Then draw what you would look like.

If I were a fish . . .

Math Practice: Fractions

Write the fraction for the shaded part.

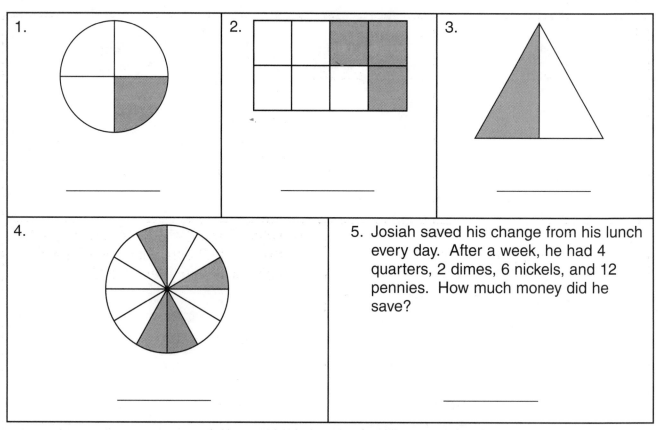

1.

2.

3.

4.

5. Josiah saved his change from his lunch every day. After a week, he had 4 quarters, 2 dimes, 6 nickels, and 12 pennies. How much money did he save?

Language Practice: Adjectives

Unscramble each word to find an adjective. Then take the letters that are circled and fill them in order inside the boxes to find the message.

lamsl

eicn

shtor

clcethooa

erlya

ghhi

lysil

nnyuf

gunoy

renge

Message

Writing Practice: Write a paragraph describing what you would like to be when you become an adult.

Name _____

Math Practice: Mixed Computation

Solve each problem.

1. 426 + 879	2. 3,024 − 1,883	3. 552 x 6
4. 7)49	5. Isaiah planted 4 rows of beans. Each row had 23 bean plants. How many bean plants are there in all? _____	

Language Practice: Dictionary Skills

Circle all words you would find on a dictionary page with these guide words.

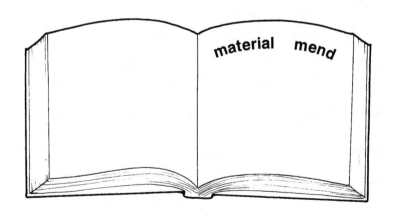

material   mend

measure	match
memory	meet
menial	medical
mean	merge
matron	master
matter	mate

 Writing Practice: Write a story about watching a scary movie on television on a stormy night.

Name _____

Math Practice: Multiplication Including Money

Solve each problem.

1.   471
      x 8
	2. 652
	      x 3
		3. $21.18
		      x 4

4.
$7.98
x 5

5. Shawn had $20.00. He buys a sweater for $12.99 and socks for $2.99. What will his change be when he pays for his clothes?

_____

Language Practice: Capitalization

Circle which group of names below are capitalized correctly.

1. Mrs. melba Moore
   mrs. melba moore
   Mrs. Melba Moore

2. Chanori and I
   chanori and I
   Chanori and i

3. Dr. D.l. moody
   Dr. D.L. Moody
   Dr. D.L. moody

4. Dequan Williams, Jr.
   dequan williams, jr.
   Dequan Williams, jr.

5. Aunt Jill
   aunt Jill
   aunt jill

6. mister Antonio Proctor
   Mister Antonio Proctor
   mister antonio proctor

 Writing Practice: Your class gets a new student. He has never worked with a computer before, so your teacher says you can show him how to use the Internet. Write a paragraph about what you would tell him about the computer.

Name _____

Practice 42

Math Practice: Division

Divide the smaller number into the larger number and then solve problem 5.

1.　49, 7 _____	2.　5, 50 _____	3.　32, 8 _____
4.　4, 24 _____	5. Kyoto brought a bag of candy to a class party. The bag had enough candy for every student to get two pieces. There were 31 students in the class. How many pieces of candy were in the bag? _____

Language Practice: Homographs

Choose the sentence that goes with the picture.

1. We need to train our dog.

2. The train jumped the track.

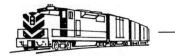 _____

3. The boss lashes out at his employees.

4. A camel's lashes protect his eyes.

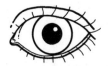 _____

5. The dog brought back the stick.

6. Yong tried to stick his finger.

 _____

7. The glass in the window broke.

8. I filled my glass up with milk.

 _____

 Writing Practice: Write a paragraph about what you think it takes to be a successful student.

©Teacher Created Materials, Inc.　　　45　　　#3302 Daily Skills Practice—Grades 4–5

Math Practice: Fractions

Fill in the blanks with the missing number. Then solve problem 5.

1. $\dfrac{1}{4} = \dfrac{\quad}{16}$	2. $\dfrac{3}{5} = \dfrac{\quad}{20}$	3. $\dfrac{5}{4} = \dfrac{\quad}{16}$
4. $\dfrac{2}{3} = \dfrac{\quad}{12}$	5. Brittani had 13 goldfish. Her mother bought her 6 more. The next day she found 2 dead. Then a week later one fish had 12 babies. How many goldfish does she now have? _____	

Language Practice: Prefixes

Circle each word with a prefix.

happiness	unclear	redone
jumping	helpless	preseason
careful	mender	disadvantage
misinterpret	capable	mistake

 Writing Practice: Write a paragraph using the sentence starter below.

When I get home from school, I . . .

Name _____

Math Practice: Fractions

Write <, >, or = between each fraction and then solve problem 5.

1.
$\frac{2}{4}$ ◯ $\frac{4}{8}$

2.
$\frac{5}{8}$ ◯ $\frac{3}{8}$

3.
$\frac{4}{8}$ ◯ $\frac{6}{12}$

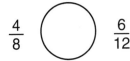

4.
$\frac{2}{10}$ ◯ $\frac{5}{20}$

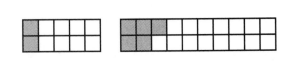

5. Aimee and her three friends ordered a pizza.

If they cut the pizza into 10 slices, how many pieces will each person get?

_____

Will there be any left over?

_____

If so, how many? _____

Language Practice: Homographs

Write two sentences with each word showing different meanings.

1. star _____

_____

2. light _____

_____

3. letter _____

_____

4. stamp _____

_____

Writing Practice: Write a paragraph explaining why schools have rules.

Name _____

Math Practice: Rounding

Round to the place value that is underlined. Then solve number 5.

1. 6,<u>7</u>89	2. 5,3<u>2</u>9	3. 9<u>8</u>2
_____	_____	_____

4. 2<u>3</u>,087	5. Roberto lives 134 miles from the nearest mountain. Round this distance to the nearest 10 miles.
_____	_____

Language Practice: Suffixes

Underline each word that contains a suffix.

comfortable	foolish	uncover
unwrap	prepaid	teacher
argument	singer	election
laziness	finalist	jumping
prearrange	careless	beautiful

Writing Practice: Write a story about the wildest dream you've ever had.

Name _____

Math Practice: Multiplication

Fill in the blanks. Then solve problem 5.

1. _____ x 3 = 24	2. 4 x _____ = 8	3. 6 x _____ = 42
4. _____ x 9 = 72	5. Darrell has 13 pencils. He gave 8 to Jorge. He then found enough pencils to double what he had left. How many pencils does Darrell have now? _____	

Language Practice: Spelling

Circle the correctly spelled word.

1. receive	recieve	5. wierd	weird
2. misspell	mispell	6. procede	proceed
3. calender	calendar	7. thier	their
4. vacuum	vaccum	8. believe	beleive

 Writing Practice: Write a paragraph with the sentence starter below.

This weekend I had the most fun when . . .

Name _____

Math Practice: Multiplication

Solve each problem.

1.	2.	3.
34 x 6	65 x 5	123 x 4

4.	5. Sherry had 4 pairs of white socks, 5 pairs of black socks, and 6 pairs of brown socks.
456 x 2	How many pairs of socks did Sherry have? _____ Since a pair is two, count each sock. How many socks is that? _____

Language Practice: Spelling

Rewrite each misspelled word correctly.

1. auther _____   6. tommorrow _____

2. frite _____   7. twelth _____

3. abcense _____   8. suprise _____

4. certian _____   9. cheif _____

5. Wendesday _____   10. fourty _____

 Writing Practice: Write a paragraph about the best birthday you ever had.

Math Practice: Division

Solve each problem.

1. $2\overline{)14}$	2. $5\overline{)36}$	3. $3\overline{)36}$
4. $6\overline{)52}$	5. Four buses were driven to school. There were 52 students on each bus. How many students were on all four buses? _____	

Language Practice: Homographs

Write two sentences with each homograph showing different meanings. Then think of one more homograph and write two sentences with it.

1. rose _____

   _____

2. leaves _____

   _____

3. _____ _____

   _____

 Writing Practice: Write a story about visiting a farm and seeing farm animals up close.

Name _____

Math Practice: Multiplication and Division with Money

Solve each problem.

1. $1.29 x 3	2. $3.42 x 6	3. 6)$3.60
4. 7)$4.20	5. There were 28 people in Ruth's class. There were 12 boys. How many were girls? _____	

Language Practice: Subjects and Predicates

Circle the subject and underline the predicate in each sentence.

1. My friends and I went trick-or-treating.

2. I was a spooky ghost.

3. Our neighbors gave us lots of candy.

4. Jordan tripped over his costume.

5. We ran and jumped all the way down the street.

6. Halloween is a time to have fun with your friends.

 Writing Practice: Write an informative paragraph for the school newspaper about the school dance in two weeks.

Math Practice: Multiplication with Money

Solve each problem.

1. $1.63 x 9	2. $2.41 x 8	3. $16.84 x 5
4. $27.15 x 4	5. Suo Yao bought 5 pairs of earrings for her mother. They cost $5.64 for each pair of earrings. How much did she spend? _____	

Language Practice: Kinds of Sentences

Read the following sentences. Write **D** if the sentence is Declarative, **I** for Imperative, **E** for Exclamatory, or **INT** for Interrogative. Then place the correct punctuation mark at the end of the sentence.

1. _____ How many pencils did Juan have ___

2. _____ Give me one of your pencils, Jamal ___

3. _____ Sheryln bought a dozen pencils at the bookstore ___

4. _____ She gave each girl in her class a pencil ___

5. _____ Mrs. Sagrages exclaimed, "What a nice gesture ___"

6. _____ Javier asked, "Why didn't the boys get a pencil ___"

Writing Practice: Write an invitation inviting your friends to a Halloween party.

Name _____

Math Practice: Place Value

Circle the answer to each problem. Then solve problem 5.

1. Which number is five thousand, seven hundred eighty-six?	2. Which is the number for ten thousand, five?	3. Which number is 900 + 9?
a. 5,786 c. 50,768 b. 5,768 d. 50,786	a. 10,050 c. 10,005 b. 1,050 d. 1,005	a. 9,909 c. 909 b. 9,009 d. 990

4. Which number is 20,000 + 5,000 + 70 + 3?	5. Earth orbits the sun once in 365 days. How long would it take Earth to orbit the sun 25 times?
a. 25,703 c. 20,573 b. 25,073 d. 25,730	_____

Language Practice: Punctuation

Choose the correct punctuation mark (. ? !) for each sentence.

1. Do not pick the daisies____

2. Where are the shovels____

3. Can you hear the woodpecker____

4. Ouch, these thorns are very sharp____

5. She is planting seeds____

6. What a beautiful day to work in the garden____

 Writing Practice: Write a paragraph about what you like or dislike about the month of November.

Math Practice: Patterns

Complete the pattern. Then solve number 5.

1. 50, 47, 44, 41, _____	2. 5, 9, 13, 17, 21, _____	3. *, U, U, #, *, U, U, #, _____
4. GH, HI, IJ, JK, KL, _____	5. Mrs. Adams wants to buy pencils for each student in her class. If the pencils are $0.12 each, how much money will she spend for her 28 students? _____	

Language Practice: Subject

Write the simple subject of each sentence in the space provided.

_____ 1. Mr. Keith took our class on a hike.

_____ 2. We saw a lot of traffic.

_____ 3. Jose pointed to an unusual building.

_____ 4. Three girls stopped at an old fountain.

_____ 5. The sun was shining brightly.

_____ 6. Look at the dog in the middle of the street.

_____ 7. The class came back to school at 3:00.

 Writing Practice: Write a short story about getting a haircut and it not being the haircut you wanted. Tell what it looked like and what you did.

Name _____

Math Practice: Mixed Computation

For numbers 1–4, copy each problem vertically. Then solve the problems.

1. 47,508 + 16,893 =	2. 7,203 – 805 =	3. 842 x 7 =

4. 93 ÷ 6 =	5. Wesley needs 6 ounces of paint for each model car he makes. If he has a 30 ounce can of paint, how many cars can he paint? _____

Language Practice: Predicate

Underline the predicate of each sentence.

1. Our family went on a vacation to the mountains.

2. We rented a cabin and stayed in the forest.

3. One night I heard a bear outside my window.

4. The bear was going through the garbage cans.

5. The next morning, trash was everywhere!

6. We stayed in the mountains for three more days.

7. Would you like to see a bear?

 Writing Practice: Write a paragraph using the title below.

Things I've Always Wanted but Never Had

Math Practice: Division

Solve each problem.

1. $6\overline{)36}$	2. $9\overline{)810}$	3. $4\overline{)284}$
4. $5\overline{)450}$	5. The students in Mr. Marcos' class bought school supplies for their class. They bought 3 packs of paper at $0.69 each, 12 pencils at $0.09 each, and 6 bottles of glue at $0.49 each. How much did all the supplies cost? _____	

Language Practice: Parts of a Friendly Letter

Name the parts of a friendly letter.

Keli Smith
328 Village St.
Anytown, USA 87654   1. _____

Dear Jane,   2. _____

    How are you doing? I've been thinking about you ever since you moved to Anytown. Do you like your new school? How is your new house? Have you found any new friends?   3. _____

    Maybe you could come visit me during the summer. Talk to your mother about it. Write me back. I miss you!

                    Love,   4. _____
                    Keli   5. _____

 Writing Practice: Your best friend just moved away. Write a letter to him or her. Don't forget to write about what you are doing since he or she moved away.

Name _____

Math Practice: Multiplication

Solve each problem.

1. 46 x 8	2. 102 x 8	3. 16 x 32

4. 22 x 24	5. Shelia wanted to buy stickers for her sticker book. They cost $.05 each. How many stickers can she buy with $2.15? _____

Language Practice: Addressing an Envelope

Address the envelope with the following addresses:

- Return address: Write your own name and address.
- Address the letter to: Marcus Chatham, 409 McDonald Dr., St. Clair, PA 12390

 Writing Practice: Write a paragraph about things you've always wanted to do but never got to do.

Name _____

Math Practice: Roman Numerals

Write the Roman numerals for the following numbers. Then solve problem 5.

1. 25 = _____	2. 32 = _____	3. 105 = _____

4. 91 = _____	5. If Francisco had XXII oranges and sold XIV, how many would he have left? Write the number in Roman numerals. _____

Language Practice: Consonant Blends

Circle the consonant blends in each of these words.

1. comprise
2. sprout
3. stranger
4. previous

5. split
6. instruct
7. immigration
8. surprise

9. stapler
10. spoon
11. scrub
12. splat

 Writing Practice: Write a story using the sentence starter below.

Last night I . . .

Math Practice: Geometry

Find the perimeter. Then solve problem number 5.

1.

6 ft.

2 ft.

P = _____

2.

4 ft.

P = _____

3.

12 in.

P = _____

4.

8 cm

12 cm

P = _____

5. Barney went on vacation with his family. They traveled 125 miles the first day, and 201 miles the second day. By the end of the third day, they had traveled a total of 500 miles. How many miles did they travel the third day?

_____

Language Practice: Subject and Predicate

Circle the subject and underline the predicate in each sentence.

1. Mr. Jones gave us a Christmas present.

2. We opened it up on Christmas morning.

3. My brother received a toy truck.

4. My present was a board game.

5. Christmas makes me feel good inside.

Writing Practice: Write a paragraph using the sentence starter below.

I'm going to have fun this holiday season because . . .

Math Practice: Measurement

Circle the larger unit. Then solve problem number 5.

1. 4 in. or 4 ft.	2. 74 yd. or 74 mi.	3. 1 yd. or 1 in.
4. 60 ft. or 60 in.	5. Students at Gladeville Middle School collected 23 lbs. of aluminum cans, 18 lbs. of plastic bottles, and 78 lbs. of newspapers for the annual recycling drive. How many pounds of recycling material did they collect in all? _____	

Language Practice: Syllables

How many syllables does each word have? Write each word under the correct heading.

library

table

magazine

paper

globe

reference

shelf

computer

book

One	Two	Three

 Writing Practice: Write a paragraph using the sentence starter below.

I walked into a jungle and saw . . .

Math Practice: Measurement

Write the correct measurement (in., ft., yd., or mi.). Then solve number 5.

1. the depth of a swimming pool _____	2. the distance to Mars _____	3. the width of your hand _____
4. the material in a dress _____	5. D'Andre worked on his homework after school. He started at 4:15 P.M. and finished right before supper at 6:00 P.M. How long did he work on his homework? _____	

Language Practice: Compound Sentences

Combine the two simple sentences with a comma and a connecting word to make a compound sentence.

1. Joellyn woke up late. She was late to school.

   _____

2. She told her teacher she was late. She had overslept.

   _____

3. Mrs. Sagraves was teaching math. She was giving directions.

   _____

   _____

4. Her teacher said to sit down quickly. She had to take off her coat.

   _____

   _____

5. She sat down. She worked very hard.

   _____

 Writing Practice: Write a paragraph about a time you were late to school.

62

Math Practice: Subtraction

Solve each problem.

1. 841 − 30	2. 644 − 132	3. 891 − 105
4. 85 − 18	5. Jim has to leave for school at 7:30 A.M. It is 6:45 A.M. How long does he have before he leaves for school? _____	

Language Practice: Sequencing

Put these sentences in order by looking at the time-order words.

_____ When we got there, we checked into the hotel and unpacked our bags.

_____ There we rode rides and saw Mickey Mouse.

_____ Then we went for a swim.

_____ My family and I went to Florida.

_____ Finally, we left all tired and worn out.

_____ Next, we changed clothes and left for Disney World.

Writing Practice: Write a paragraph using the sentence starter below.

Rainy days make me feel . . .

Name _____

Math Practice: Geometry

Write *point*, *ray*, *line segment*, or *line* in the correct box. Then solve problem 5.

1. ●————● _____	2. ● _____	3. ←————→ _____

4. ●———→ _____	5. Derek saw 32 birds. Natasha saw 18 birds. How many more birds did Derek see than Natasha? _____

Language Practice: Homonyms

Fill in the blanks with the correct *to*, *too*, or *two*.

1. Sally has _____ dolls.

2. Hailey has the same amount of dolls, _____.

3. They like _____ play with their dolls.

4. "Let's go _____ the store and buy _____ more," said Sally.

5. "That's _____ bad," said Hailey's mother, "because we have _____ eat dinner."

 Writing Practice: Write a speech to convince your classmates that you would make a good class president.

Math Practice: Subtraction with Money

Solve each problem.

1.	2.	3.
$10.20 − $ 3.42	$8.74 − $3.65	$27.19 − $18.03

4.	5. Sue bought a sweater for $13.47. She gave the cashier $20.00. What was her change?
$4.03 − $1.87	_____

Language Practice: Proofreading Skills

Write each sentence correctly.

1. i go to tom joy elementary school _____

2. the fourth grade will be a goode yer _____

3. the robin be mine favorite bird _____

4. all birds has feather said matt _____

5. jim please right there names _____

6. we red a play at schol this weak _____

7. three duck swimmed in the pond _____

8. i saw an mother duck and her babys _____

 Writing Practice: If you could change anything about your life, what would it be? Write a paragraph explaining your wishes.

Name _____

Math Practice: Mixed Computation

Solve each problem.

1.	2.	3.
483 + 849	400 − 263	25 x 14

4.

6) 892

5. Barbara plans to buy a tennis racket for $26.00 and shoes for $13.00.

How much does she plan to spend?

_____

If she has $50.00 to spend, will she have enough money left over to buy a can of tennis balls for $3.97? _____

Language Practice: Proofreading Skills

Write each sentence correctly.

1. when do mary walk her dog _____

2. she walk's scruffy at 400 pm _____

3. how much do a hamburger costs _____

4. julie bout french fries, and a soda _____

5. yesterday we had homework in spelling math and reading _____

_____

6. the first monday in september is labor day_____

_____

7. were going to my grandma house said john_____

_____

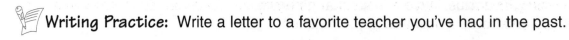 **Writing Practice:** Write a letter to a favorite teacher you've had in the past.

Math Practice: Addition and Subtraction with Money

Solve each problem.

1. $4.20 + $3.99	**2.** $28.99 + $41.35	**3.** $10.50 − $ 5.42
4. $58.14 − $26.25	**5.** The product of two numbers is 24. The sum of the same two numbers is 11. What are the two numbers? _____	

Language Practice: Homonyms

Circle the correct homonym for each sentence.

1. I went to the dentist (four, for) a check-up today.

2. He said I had (four, for) cavities.

3. My mom likes to (sew, so) clothes for my doll.

4. I want to make good grades, (sew, so) I study for my tests.

5. The sky is a light-colored (blew, blue).

6. Jessie (blew, blue) his trumpet in band class.

7. The (be, bee) on the sunflower was a bright yellow and black in color.

8. Mom said we should leave it alone and let it (be, bee).

 Writing Practice: Write a story about playing outside when suddenly you see an angry bee heading towards you.

Math Practice: Geometry and Measurement

Find the perimeter. Then, solve problem 5.

1. P = _____ 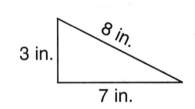 3 in., 8 in., 7 in.	2. P = _____ 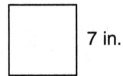 7 in.	3. P = _____ 6 cm
4. P = _____ 4 ft. 10 ft.	5. At basketball games, there are 20 rows of seats with 24 seats in each row. How many people can be seated at games? _____

Language Practice: Syllables

Divide these words into syllables.

1. entire

_____

2. commercial

_____

3. appoint

_____

4. favorite

_____

5. magazine

_____

6. goblet

_____

7. wriggle

_____

8. together

_____

9. because

_____

10. tomorrow

_____

11. attention

_____

12. laughter

_____

 Writing Practice: Write a paragraph to complete this idea.

I wish it would snow because . . .

Name _____

Practice 66

Math Practice: Subtraction

Solve each problem.

1. $40.40 – $12.98	2. 1,620 – 1,598	3. $30.05 – $ 8.67
4. 3,000 – 1,542	5. Mrs. Morgan bought her students Christmas gifts that totaled $16.98. What is her change if she pays with $20.00? _____	

Language Practice: Cause and Effect

Tell which part of the sentence is the cause and which is the effect. Write **C** if it is the cause; write **E** if it is the effect.

1. _____ Because of playing in the rain, I got a bad cold _____.

2. _____ To make good grades, I study hard and do my homework _____.

3. _____ We went to the zoo because our class won a contest _____.

4. _____ I went to bed early so I could get up in time for school _____.

5. _____ Since Tory and Alfonzo are good friends, they play at each other's house _____.

6. _____ I have to write Don a letter, because he moved to Illinois _____.

 Writing Practice: If you could meet any famous person, who would it be, and why? Write a paragraph explaining your answer.

Math Practice: Mixed Computation

Solve each problem.

1.	2.	3.
241 362 + 103	2,000 − 1,782	4,553 x 4

4.	5. Joe and Jeff entered the 100 yard dash in the school race. Joe practiced 1 hour a day for 5 weeks, and Jeff practiced 2 hours a day for 3 weeks. Who spent more time practicing for the race?
7)498	_____

Language Practice: Nouns

Circle the nouns in the following paragraph.

My Pet

I have a pet named Scruffy. He is a special dog called a Lab. He came to live at our house nine years ago. You should have seen him. He was a puppy and was so small. He weighed only 3 pounds. He is a good dog and never barks. He is also very cute, especially when he sleeps. My family has enjoyed having a pet like Scruffy.

Writing Practice: Write a story about a pet you have. If you don't have a pet, write a story about a pet you would like to have.

Math Practice: Rounding

Round to the nearest 10 for problems 1–4. Then solve number 5.

1. 26	2. 79	3. 452
_____	_____	_____

4. 1,658	5. Ellen made an 89, 92, 97, 88, and 100 on her spelling tests. What is her average of all 5 grades?
_____	_____

Language Practice: Adjectives

Choose the correct adjective in each sentence.

1. That is the (badest, worst) accident I've ever seen.

2. She is the (goodest, best) student in the class.

3. Marty has the (silliest, sillyest) sense of humor.

4. Who is (smartest, smarter), Joanna or Ellen?

5. Which sister is (shorter, shortest), Joy or Jill?

6. I have the (higher, highest) grades in my math class.

7. Max is (funnier, funniest) than his brother Malcolm.

8. We should be (carefuller, more careful) when playing close to the street.

 Writing Practice: Finish this story.

Joan wanted to give her mom a present, but she didn't have any money. So she decided to . . .

Math Practice: Addition

Solve the problems.

1. $7{,}283$ $3{,}854$ $+\,9{,}103$	2. 987 986 $+\,985$	3. 682 607 $+\,643$
4. $2{,}218$ $3{,}210$ $+\,4{,}216$	5. Kenisha bought 2 folders for 29 cents each, 2 pencils for 12 cents each, and notebook paper for 39 cents. She had $5.00. What would be her change? _____	

Language Practice: Predicate (Verb)

Write a sentence with each verb.

1. has taken _____

2. bought _____

3. has flown _____

4. went _____

5. have seen _____

6. walked _____

7. was going _____

8. is _____

 Writing Practice: Write a paragraph using the sentence starter below.

Playing in the snow is fun because . . .

Math Practice: Number Order

Write in order from least to greatest for problems 1–4. Then solve problem 5.

1.   13,765   13,705
      13,775   13,567
 	
 _____, _____,
 _____, _____
	2. 206 260
	      252 210
	
	 _____, _____,
	 _____, _____

3.   6,566   6,565
     6,656   6,660

_____, _____,
_____, _____

4.   1,042   1,240
       1,402   1,024

_____, _____,
_____, _____

5. Margaret played basketball for the school's team. During the first six games, she scored 11 points, 8 points, 24 points, 16 points, 9 points, and 15 points. How many points did she score in all six games?

_____

Language Practice: Predicate (Verb)

Write the tenses of the following verbs:

	Past	**Past Participle**
Example: write	wrote	written
1. sing	_____	_____
2. go	_____	_____
3. blow	_____	_____
4. give	_____	_____
5. do	_____	_____

Writing Practice: Now choose one verb above and write a paragraph with all three tenses of the verb.

Name _____

Math Practice: Rounding

Round to the nearest place. Then solve problem 5.

1. tens place 176 = _____	2. hundreds place 349 = _____	3. ones place $3.69 = _____
4. thousands place 8,764 = _____	5. Jeff needs 15 quarts of potting soil. He can only find 4-quart bags. How many 4-quart bags will he need? _____ How much will not be used? _____	

Language Practice: Predicate (Verb)

Fill in the blank with the correct tense of *run.*

1. I _____ yesterday.

2. I will _____ on Friday.

3. I have _____ in a race before.

4. Seth will _____ in a marathon next week.

5. He _____ in a marathon last year.

6. They have _____ many miles to get in shape.

Writing Practice: Write a paragraph using the sentence starter below.

If I could plan my own day at school, I would . . .

Math Practice: Decimals

Write a decimal for problems 1–4. Then solve problem 5.

1. $\frac{9}{100}$ _____	2. forty-eight and seven hundredths _____	3. 2 $\frac{7}{10}$ _____
4. nine and three tenths _____	5. If you could only buy one shirt, and the price was 2 for \$12.50, how much would one shirt be? _____	

Language Practice: Pronouns

Choose a pronoun from the box to take the place of the underlined noun. Write the pronoun on the line after the sentence. Capitalize when necessary.

we	it	they	he	their	she	him	her	our

1. Mr. Griffin is our band teacher. _____

2. Paul and I play the trumpet. _____

3. Everyone likes Mr. Griffin because he is a good teacher. _____

4. Mr. Griffin says that all students need to practice every day._____

5. Megan plays the flute. _____

6. Megan thinks Megan's playing has improved. _____

7. Mr. Griffin hopes the students' chance of winning the competition will be good.

_____

Writing Practice: Parades are always fun to watch. Write a story about watching a parade. Be sure to include all the things you see and hear.

Name _____

Math Practice: Equivalent Numbers

Write < or > between each number for problems 1–4. Then solve problem 5.

1.

15,767 ◯ 157.67

2.

2,075 ◯ 20.75

3.

176.7 ◯ 1,767

4.

30,972 ◯ 309,720

5. Using the chart below, imagine that you have $8.00 to spend. List what you would buy. Make sure you have not spent more than $8.00.

SALE
Dolls $2.52 _____
Puzzles $1.25 _____
Books $1.75 _____
Cars $1.58 _____
Wagons $4.50 _____

Language Practice: Handwriting

Copy the poem below in your best cursive handwriting.

I Do Love Math

I do love math,
I think it is fun.
I like to do problems
And get them done.
When I do math,
I feel so good.
I do so well,
I think you could.

_____ (title)

_____
_____
_____
_____
_____
_____
_____

✍ **Writing Practice:** Who or what makes you laugh? Explain this person or thing in a paragraph, and tell why you laugh.

Math Practice: Magic Squares

All rows, both horizontal and vertical, when added up will equal the stated sum. Fill in the missing numbers in the puzzle. Then solve number 5.

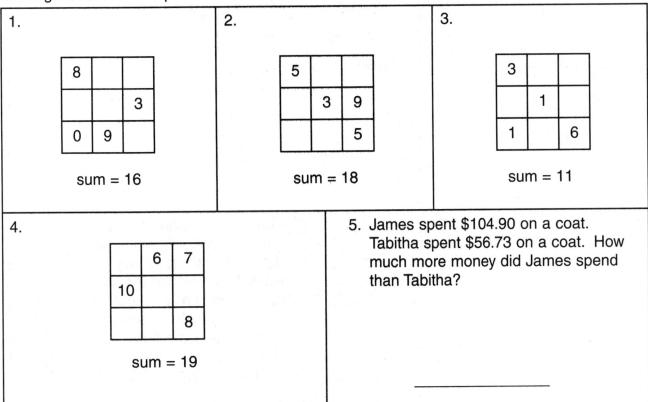

1.

8		
		3
0	9	

sum = 16

2.

5		
	3	9
		5

sum = 18

3.

3		
	1	
1		6

sum = 11

4.

	6	7
10		
		8

sum = 19

5. James spent $104.90 on a coat. Tabitha spent $56.73 on a coat. How much more money did James spend than Tabitha?

_____

Language Practice: Spelling

There is a misspelled word in each sentence. Circle the misspelled word and write the correct spelling in the blank beside the sentence.

1. Have you studyed for the test?   _____

2. It was cloudyr yesterday than today.   _____

3. Are you worryed about the exam?   _____

4. Johnny caried the trash to the dumpster.   _____

5. Do you have any hobies?   _____

6. Nashville and Knoxville are large cityes.   _____

7. Martha is the prettest girl I know.   _____

8. I copyed my homework down today.   _____

 Writing Practice: Write a newspaper article about your favorite team in baseball, basketball, or football.

Math Practice: Decimals

Add or subtract each decimal. Be sure to line up your numbers by the decimal points. Then solve problem 5.

1. 10.2 + 3.61 = _____	2. 171.16 – 15.95 = _____	3. 9.73 – 4.1 = _____
4. 102.65 + 203.1 = _____	5. Frank wants to buy a video game that costs $59.99. His mom gave him $24.00 for raking leaves for two weekends. His uncle gave him $14.00 for helping him clean out the basement. Frank already had saved $20.00. Does Frank have enough money to buy the video game? _____ If not, how much more does he need? _____	

Language Practice: Contractions

Match the contraction with the words it stands for.

will not	she's
could not	it's
I am	won't
we will	they're
cannot	couldn't
it is	I'll
we are	can't
she is	I'm
they are	we'll
I will	we're

 Writing Practice: If you could be someone famous in history, who would it be and why? Write a paragraph explaining your choice.

Math Practice: Mixed Computation

Solve each problem.

1. $\begin{array}{r} 746 \\ 832 \\ +\ 295 \\ \hline \end{array}$	2. $\begin{array}{r} 6,035 \\ -\ 2,475 \\ \hline \end{array}$	3. $\begin{array}{r} 1,271 \\ \times\ \ \ \ \ 9 \\ \hline \end{array}$

4.

$$4\overline{)144}$$

5. Jan sold 120 boxes of Girl Scout Cookies. Sharyn sold 109 boxes, and Alex sold 283.

How many boxes did they sell in all?

_____

How many more boxes did Alex sell than both Jan and Sharyn together?

_____

Language Practice: Possessive or Contraction

Write a sentence showing the correct usage of each word.

1. its _____

2. it's _____

3. their _____

4. they're _____

5. your _____

6. you're _____

Writing Practice: Write a paragraph using the title below.

What I Learned from a Grandparent

Math Practice: Multiplication

Solve each problem.

1. $$\begin{array}{r} 23 \\ \times\ 27 \\ \hline \end{array}$$	2. $$\begin{array}{r} 98 \\ \times\ 23 \\ \hline \end{array}$$	3. $$\begin{array}{r} 46 \\ \times\ 25 \\ \hline \end{array}$$

4. $$\begin{array}{r} 43 \\ \times\ 18 \\ \hline \end{array}$$	5. Tim and Jill ordered French fries. There were 36 fries in the packet. If Tim ate 13 and Jill ate 11, how many more fries would each of them eat if they ate the same number of additional fries? _____

Language Practice: Predicate

Circle each action verb below.

shirt	punches	hat	child	leaped	sing
cape	run	reads	shoes	kicks	suit
wishes	eye	dishes	washes	flew	sky

✏️ **Writing Practice:** Write a paragraph using the sentence starter below.

My goal for the New Year is . . .

Name _____

Math Practice: Multiplication

Solve each problem.

1. 340 x 2	2. 176 x 4	3. 226 x 3
4. $1.92 x 5	5. Carlos has $10.00 to spend on a gift for his brother. He buys a football for $3.99 and also buys a helmet. If his change is $1.02, how much did the helmet cost? _____	

Language Practice: Verb Tense

Write the correct form of the verb in each sentence. The verb follows the sentence.

1. Nathan and Natalie _____ to school together. *(walk)*

2. "Something _____ funny," I said as we got to school. *(smell)*

3. The science teacher was _____ an experiment. *(do)*

4. Our teacher _____ to get out our homework. *(say)*

5. I couldn't find my homework so I _____ in my desk. *(look)*

6. She said I could _____ it to her after math class. *(give)*

7. Renee _____ up and said, "I found it. It fell on the floor." *(stand)*

8. On the way home, a bee _____ me. *(sting)*

9. It hurt so badly that I _____, "Ouch!" *(scream)*

10. Mom put an ice pack on it, and it _____ better. *(feel)*

Writing Practice: Write a paragraph using the sentence starter below.

If I could travel anywhere in the world, it would be to . . .

Name _____

Math Practice: Subtraction

Solve each problem.

1.	2.	3.
2,000 − 1,385	$10.00 − $ 9.43	$56.00 − $19.93

4.	5. On July 4th the high temperature in Sacramento was 93°. The low temperature that evening was 67°. What was the change in temperature for that day?
7,000 − 4,928	_____

Language Practice: Adjectives

Circle the adjectives that describe a Christmas tree.

star	green
shiny	stand
present	big
beautiful	bright
ornament	round
lights	branches
sharp	under
tall	decorative

 Writing Practice: Martin Luther King, Jr. had a dream. We also have dreams or wishes. Write a paragraph with the title, "I Have a Dream."

Name _____

Math Practice: Money

Look at the prices of each baseball item. Answer the questions.

glove	$29.87
bat	$17.74
cleats	$22.00
uniform	$42.28
pair of socks	$3.97
baseball	$2.69

1. Which item cost more, the glove or the bat?

   _____

   What is the difference?

   _____

2. How much more does the uniform cost than the socks?

   _____

3. Could a player get the uniform and cleats for $50.00? _____

   How do you know?

   _____

   _____

   _____

4. How much is the total if a player buys one of each item? _____

Language Practice: Adjectives

Adjectives tell *which one*, *what kind of*, or *how many*. Write the adjectives below under each heading.

tough   one
juicy   spotted
old   red
cold   fresh
better   many
curly   black
friendly few
fast   first

Which One	What Kind Of	How Many

 Writing Practice: Write a descriptive paragraph about waking up one morning and finding yourself in a cartoon.

Math Practice: Decimals

Add the following decimals. Then solve problem 5.

1. 4.8 + 7.6 = _____	**2.** 0.05 + 0.39 = _____	**3.** 10.29 + 16.90 = _____
4. 45.0 + 34.28 = _____	**5.** Andrew bought a basketball for $5.39. He had enough money to buy a pair of basketball shoes for $21.97. How much did Andrew spend? _____ How much is his change if he paid with a $20 bill and a $10 bill? _____	

Language Practice: Adverbs

Adverbs tell *how*, *when*, or *where*. Write each adverb under the correct heading.

slowly   near

always   happily

never   far

daily   well

fast   quickly

friendly   here

today   there

How	When	Where

 Writing Practice: Write a short story with the title, "The Holiday Season is a Time for Giving."

Math Practice: Measurement

Circle the more reasonable temperature. Then solve problem 5.

1. football weather	2. hot cocoa	3. a store during the summer
20° F 50° F	32° F 82° F	50° F 70° F

4. soup	5. The temperature was 29° C. It rose 15°. What is the temperature now?
52° F 72° F	_____

Language Practice: Contractions

Choose the correct word in the parentheses.

1. We (doesn't, don't) like to eat spinach.

2. I (doesn't, don't) want to wash the dishes.

3. They (wasn't, weren't) going to the mall today.

4. She (wasn't, weren't) honest with Bill.

5. We (aren't, isn't) supposed to talk during class.

6. He (aren't, isn't) sure what to do in math.

Writing Practice: Write a paragraph about living on a space station.

Math Practice: Reading a Graph

Study the graph and answer the questions.

1. How many chocolate ice cream cones were sold? _____	2. Which flavor of ice cream sold the most? _____	3. How many more strawberry cones were sold than vanilla cones? _____
4. How many ice cream cones were sold in all? _____	**Ice Cream Cones Sold on Sunday** Chocolate Vanilla Strawberry Sherbet 🍦 = 10 cones	

Language Practice: Punctuation

Add a colon (:) or a semicolon (;) to each sentence.

1. Shari felt funny ___ her stomach hurt.

2. She had just been to the fair ___ it was fun.

3. She rode many rides ___ the ferris wheel, the swings, and the bumper cars.

4. Shari had eaten before the rides ___ it was a mistake.

5. Shari ate these foods ___ popcorn, a hot dog, two sodas, and cotton candy.

6. She knew her mom would come home at 5___00.

Writing Practice: Write about what you like and dislike about where you live.

Name _____

Math Practice: Magic Squares

All rows, both horizontal and vertical, when added up will equal the sum. Fill in the missing numbers in the squares.

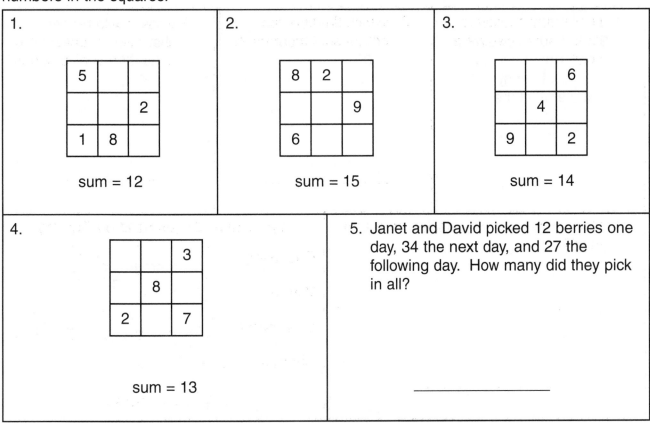

1.

5		
		2
1	8	

sum = 12

2.

8	2	
		9
6		

sum = 15

3.

		6
	4	
9		2

sum = 14

4.

		3
	8	
2		7

sum = 13

5. Janet and David picked 12 berries one day, 34 the next day, and 27 the following day. How many did they pick in all?

_____

Language Practice: Plurals

Write the plural forms of each word under the correct title.

tray   berry
cowboy   fly
penny   journey
city   key
fry   buy
way   cry
turkey   lady

y + s	y to i and add es

 Writing Practice: Write a story about your pet being able to talk, so you become famous. What do you do? Tell about your adventures.

Math Practice: Money

Solve the problems.

1. If a wristband cost $1.39 and a headband cost $1.85, how much will it cost Jenny to buy both items at the store? _____	2. What would be Jenny's change if she paid with $5.00? _____	3. What would be her change if she paid with $10.00? _____
4. Could Jenny buy two of each item with $7.00? _____	5. There are 24 hours in one day. How many hours are in $\frac{1}{2}$ of a day? _____ In 3 days? _____	

Language Practice: Consonant Blends

Choose the correct blend (**CH**, **SH**, **TH**) to complete each word.

1. BEA ___ ___

2. FLA ___ ___

3. ___ ___ AIN

4. REA ___ ___

5. PEA ___ ___

6. ___ ___ AIR

7. ___ ___ OVEL

8. ___ ___ ESE

9. RI ___ ___

10. ___ ___ EM

11. SQUA ___ ___

12. ___ ___ IMNEY

✎ **Writing Practice:** Do you like to take tests? Why or why not? Write about it.

Math Practice: Division with Money

Solve each problem.

1. $6)\overline{\$36.60}$	2. $3)\overline{\$98.79}$	3. $8)\overline{\$73.60}$

4. $2)\overline{\$56.92}$

5. There are 365 days in a year.

How many days are there in 9 years?

_____

How many days are there in 15 years?

_____

Language Practice: Spelling

Complete all words with correct spelling by adding **el** or **le** to the word.

1. wrigg_____   6. tow_____   11. ank_____

2. princip_____   7. purp_____   12. mot_____

3. app_____   8. cab_____   13. chann_____

4. nozz_____   9. cam_____   14. unc_____

5. marv_____   10. lev_____   15. trav_____

 Writing Practice: After eating in a Chinese restaurant, you get a fortune cookie. You open it, and to your surprise, the message was not what you expected. Write a story about the fortune you received in your cookie.

Name _____

Math Practice: Decimals

Solve each problem.

1.	2.	3.
27.83 + 9.75	96.70 − 54.82	43.03 x 6

4.	5. Miguel and his three friends found $33.60 on the ground in his yard. If they decide to split the money between each of them, how much would each person get?
8)‾20.8	_____

Language Practice: Possessives

Rewrite each group of words to make them show ownership.

1. the shoes of Josh _____

2. the desks of the students _____

3. the wings of the geese _____

4. the toys of the baby _____

5. the homework of Julie _____

6. the coats of the girls _____

7. the flowers of the florist _____

8. the leaves of the tree _____

Writing Practice: Write a paragraph using the sentence starter below.

If I had a million dollars, I would . . .

Name _____

Math Practice: Mixed Computation

Solve each problem.

1. 481 + 369 = _____	2. 4,800 – 1,469 = _____	3. 482 x 23 = _____

4. 879 ÷ 4 = _____	5. A suitcase fell off a 40-story building. Someone caught it on the 16th floor. How many stories did it fall? _____ How many stories were left before it would have hit the ground? _____

Language Practice: Abbreviations

Write the abbreviations to these units of measurement.

1. ounce _____   4. yard _____   7. gallon _____

2. inch _____   5. centimeter _____   8. pint _____

3. milligram _____   6. quart _____   9. mile _____

Next, write the words for which these abbreviations stand.

10. P.M. _____   13. min. _____   16. A.D. _____

11. A.M. _____   14. hr. _____   17. c. _____

12. sec. _____   15. B.C. _____   18. ml _____

 Writing Practice: Write a poem using the title, "If."

Math Practice: Multiplication and Division

Solve each problem.

1. 22.35 x 22	2. 1,244 x 12	3. 2)74.50
4. 2)1,555	5. Donny needs 42 birthday invitations. The invitations are sold in packages of 5. How many packages will Donny need to buy? _____ How do you know? _____ _____	

Language Practice: Dictionary Skills

The pronunciation of words are given in the dictionary. Write what letter is silent in each word. You may use a dictionary, if needed. For numbers 11–15, create your own words and write the silent letter.

1. autumn _____
2. knots _____
3. climbing _____
4. Wednesday _____
5. thumbs _____

6. know _____
7. shake _____
8. gnome _____
9. mechanic _____
10. maze _____

11. _____ _____
12. _____ _____
13. _____ _____
14. _____ _____
15. _____ _____

 Writing Practice: Write a story and use words that have silent letters in them. After you have finished writing, circle the silent letters.

Math Practice: Geometry

Find the area. Then solve problem 5.

1.

1 m

6 m

A = _____

2.

10 in.

12 in.

A = _____

3.

8 cm

A = _____

4.

8 ft.

2 ft.

A = _____

5. Joan has 120 baseball cards. She sold 87 and then bought 23 more. How many cards does she have now?

_____

Language Practice: Compound Words

Match the compound words in the boxes.

your	lash	rain	paper
honey	mark	play	shell
eye	melon	birth	noon
door	moon	after	fish
water	self	cat	ground
book	light	news	day
candle	knob	sea	bow

Writing Practice: Write five predictions about your future.

Math Practice: Decimals

Write each problem in decimals. Then solve problem 5.

1. one and two tenths	2. four and three hundredths	3. six thousandths
_____	_____	_____

4. ninety hundredths	5. Johnny Appleseed had 437 apple seeds. He planted 35 seeds in each of 7 rows.
	How many seeds did he plant? _____
_____	How many seeds did he have left? _____

Language Practice: Antonyms

Antonyms are words that have opposite meanings. Match each word below with its opposite.

_____ 1. big	a. dull		
_____ 2. happy	b. close		
_____ 3. in	c. short		
_____ 4. young	d. follower		
_____ 5. smooth	e. sad		
_____ 6. fat	f. dry		
_____ 7. bright	g. strong		
_____ 8. wet	h. skinny		
_____ 9. long	i. out		
_____ 10. weak	j. rough		
_____ 11. leader	k. old		
_____ 12. far	l. little		

Writing Practice: Write a paragraph using the sentence starter below.

If I were a teacher, I'd . . .

Math Practice: Writing Numbers

Write the word name for the following numbers and then solve problem 5.

1. 60,372	2. 50.72	3. 1,204
_____ _____ _____	_____ _____ _____	_____ _____ _____

4. 369,075	5. Chicago has 1,546,923 residents. Write that number in words.
_____ _____ _____	_____ _____ _____

Language Practice: Antonyms

Antonyms are words that have opposite meanings. Write an antonym for each word. You may use a thesaurus if needed.

1. rich _____

2. clear _____

3. down _____

4. famous _____

5. slow _____

6. loud _____

7. huge _____

8. receive _____

9. high _____

10. empty _____

11. dirty _____

12. tall _____

Writing Practice: Write a paragraph using the sentence starter below.

If I were a colonist, . . .

Math Practice: Roman Numerals

Write the Roman numeral for each number. Then solve problem 5.

1. 9 = _____	2. 50 = _____	3. 122 = _____
4. 13 = _____	5. You studied for your math quiz 15 minutes every day for a week. How long have you studied for your math quiz? _____	

Language Practice: Synonyms

Synonyms are words that have the same or similar meanings. Write a synonym for each word. You may use a thesaurus, if needed.

1. timid _____

2. sorrow _____

3. plain _____

4. cold _____

5. sound _____

6. friend _____

7. courage _____

8. right _____

9. afraid _____

10. happy _____

11. old _____

12. honest _____

 Writing Practice: Can a person be happy without having a lot of money? Write a paragraph and explain why or why not.

Math Practice: Rounding

Round to the nearest whole number and then solve problem 5.

1. 6.29 = _____	2. 1.7 = _____	3. 0.96 = _____
4. 21.39 = _____	5. Sarah, Ricardo, and Dominique rode their bikes. Sarah rode 2.1 miles, Ricardo rode 3.7 miles, and Dominique rode 5.5 miles. About how many miles did they ride altogether? Find the answer by rounding each decimal to the nearest whole number. _____	

Language Practice: Context Clues

Decide on the meaning of the underlined word in the sentences below. Circle its meaning below each sentence.

1. I used my dad's <u>shears</u> to cut a rope.
   a. knife   b. scissors   c. brush
2. His statement was <u>muddled</u> and could not be understood.
   a. knowing   b. stubborn   c. confusing
3. Carlos <u>deleted</u> his letter from the computer.
   a. removed   b. added   c. changed
4. Eagles are <u>scarce</u> because there are not many around.
   a. plentiful   b. common   c. uncommon
5. In the early morning, fog makes it looks <u>hazy</u>.
   a. cloudy   b. clear   c. sunny
6. The stick <u>jabbed</u> me in the side when I fell down.
   a. cut   b. poked   c. scraped

 Writing Practice: Write a short story about two friends running against each other in a race.

Math Practice: Logic

Read each statement and write the results.

1. Brenda, Mona, and Dennis lined up from shortest to tallest for a picture. Dennis stood between Brenda and Mona. Mona was the shortest. Who was the tallest?

   _____

2. John is eight. His sister is 12. Thomas is five years younger than John's sister. Write their names from youngest to oldest.

   _____

   _____

3. Juan is half the age of Joe. Joe is 14 years old. Tina was born five years before Juan. Tim is three times the age of Tina. List the oldest to the youngest person.

   _____

   _____

4. Stephen, Allison, Susan, and Mark sit in the same row at school. Mark sits in front of Susan. Allison sits between a girl and a boy. Stephen doesn't sit by a boy. Write, in order, where each student sits in the row, front to back.

   _____

   _____

5. There are three frogs. The spotted frog jumped 8 feet. The tree frog jumped 6 feet. The toad jumped twice as far as the tree frog. List the frogs according to their positions from shortest to farthest distance.

   _____

   _____

Language Practice: Friendly Letter and Proofreading

Make corrections on the letter below and then rewrite it on a separate sheet of paper.

192 fielder ave
ft. worth texas 97246

february 18 1999

dear charles

   hey! how are you i am fine. i looking forward to seeing you on friday. have a safe trip. When you get here we will talk about what we want to do see you then.

                    your Friend
                    michael

 Writing Practice: If you could spend the day with one of your friends, who would it be? Tell what you would do when you spend the day together.

Math Practice: Estimation and Decimals

Estimate to the nearest tenth. Then solve problem 5.

1. 5.67 = _____	2. 71.26 = _____	3. 64.74 = _____
4. 9,317.72 = _____	5. Jennifer and Marsha sold $75.63 worth of cookies. Their goal was to sell $100.00 worth. How much more would they have to sell in order to reach their goal? _____	

Language Practice: Sequencing

Number the events in time order.

1. Going to the movies
   _____ We watched the movie that started at 7:00 P.M.
   _____ Jake bought popcorn before the movie started; it was delicious.
   _____ We stood in line 20 minutes for tickets.
   _____ We went to eat at 9:00 P.M.
   _____ We each bought our own tickets.
   _____ Jake and Billy decided to go to the movies.

2. Morning routine
   _____ I get dressed.
   _____ I get up at 6:30 A.M.
   _____ My mom drives me to school.
   _____ Our family eats breakfast together.
   _____ Mom blows the horn, because I am running late.
   _____ I brush my teeth.

3. Writing a letter
   _____ Jo sealed the envelope.
   _____ I gave Jo a piece of paper to write a letter.
   _____ She asked me to mail the letter for her.
   _____ Jo put the stamp on the letter.
   _____ She wrote a letter to her grandmother.
   _____ Jo waited for an answer to her letter.

4. Making cookies
   _____ I put the cookies in the oven.
   _____ I mixed the flour, sugar, and eggs.
   _____ I measured the flour, sugar, and eggs.
   _____ I placed the ingredients on the sink.
   _____ I warmed up the oven.
   _____ I let the cookies cool so I could eat them.

Writing Practice: Write a paragraph about your evening routine each night. Make sure all sentences are in correct sentence order.

Math Practice: Even or Odd

Circle all even numbers and underline all odd numbers.

1.	2.	3.
5,403	2	444
320	99	383
43,901	2,112	97

4.	5.
72	9,008
8,896	219
45	15

Language Practice: Capitalization

Circle all words that should be capitalized.

1. mrs. vankluyve taught fifth grade last year.

2. mrs. bowman and ms. atchison are new teachers in sixth grade.

3. mrs. nelson's sister lives on the continent of europe.

4. mrs. picirilli sailed on a ship on the pacific ocean.

5. i am in mr. bryant's homeroom.

6. halloween, labor day, and thanksgiving are all fall holidays.

7. did sammy sosa hit the most home runs?

8. no, i think mark mcguire was the top home run hitter.

9. alabama is a state in the southeast.

10. there is a lake that separates the state of michigan into two parts.

 Writing Practice: Write a persuasive paragraph telling why children should or should not have to make their beds every day.

Math Practice: Money

Write what type of bills and coins equal each money value.

1. $17.53	2. $107.65	3. $75.25
_____ _____ _____	_____ _____ _____	_____ _____ _____

4. $63.71	5. Erica bought cereal for $2.39, juice for $1.59, and flour for $1.25. How much did she spend?
_____ _____ _____	_____

Language Practice: Prefix/Suffix

Add a *prefix* to each word and then write a sentence with each word.

1. _____clear   _____

2. _____do   _____

3. _____order   _____

4. _____trust   _____

Add a *suffix* to each word and then write a sentence with each word.

5. care_____   _____

6. kind_____   _____

7. sail_____   _____

8. help_____   _____

 Writing Practice: You are sleeping soundly when the phone rings and wakes you up. Write a story about what happens.

Name _____

Math Practice: Multiplication

Solve the problems.

1.	2.	3.
82 x 13	46 x 25	307 x 14

4.	5. Mrs. Stolz has 13 boxes of pencils. Each box has 24 pencils in it. How many pencils does she have in all?
224 x 63	_____

Language Practice: Plurals or Possessives

Choose the correct word to complete each sentence.

1. This recipe is for chocolate _____.
   a. cookie's   b. cookies'   c. cookies

2. It was _____ job to help with the dishes.
   a. Dads   b. Dad's   c. Dads'

3. James and Melissa saw the _____ kittens first.
   a. cat's   b. cats   c. cats'

4. Mr. Adams is a wonderful teacher who _____ fifth grade.
   a. teach's   b. teaches   c. teaches'

5. The _____ coats were hung in their lockers.
   a. students'   b. student's   c. students

 Writing Practice: Write a story about a job you would like to do when you get older. Tell why you chose that job.

Math Practice: Mixed Computation

Solve each problem.

1.	2.	3.
2,396 + 3,784	7,040 – 4,965	3,681 x 63

4.	5. Mrs. Ling wants to buy 100 pepper plants. The plants are sold in trays of 6 plants. How many trays does she need to buy?
6)5,328	_____

Language Practice: Punctuation

Choose the sentence with the correct quotation marks.

1.
   a. Emilee asked "Do you like my new outfit"?
   b. Emilee asked, "Do you like my new outfit?"
   c. Emilee asked, "do you like my new outfit?"

2.
   a. "Yes!" yelled Jodie.
   b. Yes! "yelled Jodie."
   c. "Yes! yelled Jodie."

3.
   a. "Swimming is fun" said Kevin.
   b. "Swimming is fun," said Kevin.
   c. "Swimming is fun, said Kevin."

4.
   a. Gina replied "I like to dive."
   b. "Gina replied," I like to dive.
   c. Gina replied, "I like to dive."

 Writing Practice: Write a story by finishing the statement below.

I was chosen to be a character on television. I got to play . . .

Name _____

Math Practice: Mean, Median, Mode

The students in Mr. Dahl's math class received their tests grades back. (See below for test grades.) Find the *total*, the *mean*, the *median*, and the *mode* scores.

1. Total of All Scores = _____	**2.** Mean = _____	**3.** Median = _____

4. Mode = _____	**Test Scores**	

Test Scores

Tom	97	Shelly	66
Maria	98	Howard	88
Juan	86	Lana	86
Adam	86	Eugene	93
Connie	95	Suzanne	89
Dorothy	100		

Language Practice: Dictionary Skills

Circle the word that would come between each set of guide words.

1. **perennial**   **persevere**
   a. period
   b. perspire
   c. percent

2. **cope**   **correspond**
   a. costume
   b. coordinate
   c. corps

3. **gnome**   **govern**
   a. gray
   b. gossip
   c. gnaw

4. **motorcycle**   **mule**
   a. mouth
   b. motor
   c. mull

5. **stroke**   **stuff**
   a. stretch
   b. student
   c. stump

6. **black**   **blanket**
   a. blackbird
   b. blaze
   c. blast

 Writing Practice: Write a story using the sentence starter below.

**I was playing outside when suddenly a UFO hovered over me.
I looked and . . .**

Math Practice: Geometry

Fill in the blanks with the correct answer.

A

B

C

1. In angle ABC, the vertex is _____.

2. In angle ABC, one side of the angle is

_____.

3. Angle ABC is an _____ angle.

4. Angle ABC is made up of two

_____.

Language Practice: Handwriting

Write the following quote from William Durant, the founder of General Motors, in your best handwriting.

"Forget mistakes. Forget failures. Forget everything except what you're going to do today. Today is your lucky day."

_____

_____

_____

_____

_____

 Writing Practice: Write a paragraph explaining what the quote you just wrote means to you.

Name _____

Math Practice: Fractions

Add these fractions with like denominators. Then solve problem 5.

1. $\frac{7}{8} + \frac{1}{8} = $ _____	2. $6\frac{1}{2} + 5 = $ _____	3. $3\frac{2}{7} + 1\frac{3}{7} = $ _____
4. $12\frac{7}{18} + 11\frac{2}{18} = $ _____	5. Mrs. McWilliams made treat bags for her class. She has 18 students and 86 treats. How many treats will go in each bag, if they all have equal amounts? _____	

Language Practice: Syllables

Circle the word that is correctly divided into syllables.

1.
  a. col-lect
  b. co-mmand
  c. conn-ect

2.
  a. ag-ain
  b. dis-tance
  c. exem-pt

3.
  a. harv-est
  b. gut-ter
  c. i-sland

4.
  a. mi-stake
  b. nec-klace
  c. op-tion

5.
  a. vap-or
  b. hot-el
  c. bi-son

6.
  a. pap-er
  b. sil-ver
  c. flo-wer

 Writing Practice: If you were shipwrecked on an island, what five things would you want? Be sure to tell why you chose those things.

Math Practice: Decimals

Solve each problem.

1. 97,035.6 + 33,461.2 ‾‾‾‾‾‾‾‾‾	**2.** 39.87 x .23 ‾‾‾‾‾‾‾‾	**3.** 6.470 + 3.998 ‾‾‾‾‾‾‾
4. 2.34 x .56 ‾‾‾‾‾‾‾		**5.** Janice spent $12.46 at the store on Friday and $72.90 on Saturday. How much money did Janice spend in both days? _____ How much more money did she spend on Saturday than on Friday?_____

Language Practice: Adjectives

Write an adjective (a descriptive word) in front of each noun.

1. _____ stone		6. _____ flower
2. _____ shoes		7. _____ elephant
3. _____ movie		8. _____ classroom
4. _____ baseball game		9. _____ pizza
5. _____ tree		10. _____ cake

 Writing Practice: You are the President of the United States for one day. Write a paragraph and tell about what you did and what decisions you made for the country.

Math Practice: Number Order and Writing Numbers

Follow the directions for each box.

1. Write in order from least to greatest. 47.03 4.037 470.3 47.30 4,730 _____ _____ _____	2. Write in order from greatest to least. 12.340 1,230 123.40 1,420 120.34 _____ _____ _____	3. Write the word name for this number. 4.037 _____ _____ _____

4. Write the word name for this number.

120.34

_____

_____

_____

_____

5. Read and solve the problem.

The students in Mr. Randall's class are going on a field trip. Six parents will be driving mini-vans. How many students will be riding in each van if there are 36 students?

_____

Language Practice: Proofreading

Circle all letters that should be capitalized and add commas and periods where they belong.

1. we went to the grocery store for butter eggs and cheese

2. i saw a big elephant at the st. louis zoo

3. i ate three pieces of sausage pepperoni and cheese pizza for lunch

4. sherry shouted "the house is on fire!"

5. when i get home i'll have to wash the dishes make up my bed and sweep the

   kitchen floor

 Writing Practice: You get to travel to a foreign country. Which country would you choose and why?

Math Practice: Measurement

Write which metric measure you would use to measure the following: **cm** (centimeter), **m** (meter), or **km** (kilometer). Then solve problem 5.

1. the length of your pencil	2. the length of the hallway at school	3. your height
_____	_____	_____

4. the distance from your house to school	5. You sold Teri a pencil for $0.35. She gave you a dollar.
_____	How much change does she get back? _____ She receives four coins back. What type of coins does she get back? _____ _____

Language Practice: Nouns or Verbs

Some words can be a noun or a verb, depending on the way it is used. Read the sentences below and write whether the underlined word is a *noun* or a *verb*.

1. The <u>wind</u> blew so hard, my bicycle fell over. _____

2. The string on my yo-yo got stuck, and I had to <u>wind</u> it up again. _____

3. Kindergarten students should <u>rest</u> after lunch. _____

4. The <u>rest</u> of the animals in the zoo went to sleep. _____

5. Go down the street and <u>turn</u> left onto Front Street. _____

6. Terry said, "It's my <u>turn</u>!" _____

7. Dad's <u>suit</u> was dark gray. _____

8. He said the student's homework would <u>suit</u> him. _____

9. The <u>cut</u> on his finger was bleeding. _____

10. Mrs. Roberts said not to <u>cut</u> the picture out. _____

Writing Practice: What is your favorite fairy tale? Write your own version of it.

Name _____

Math Practice: Multiplication

Fill in the squares by multiplying the numbers.

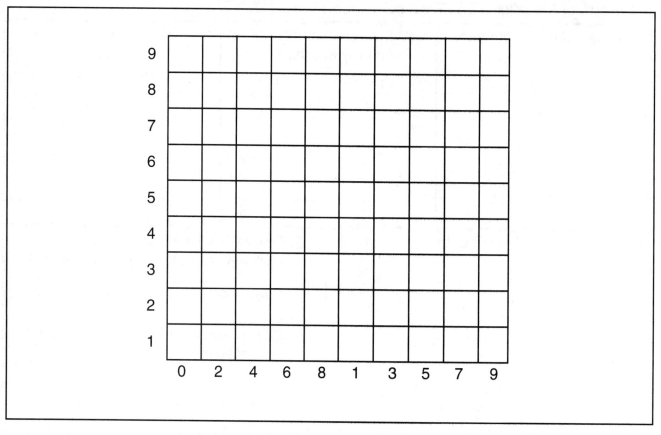

Language Practice: Dictionary Skills

Look at the page numbers and their guide words. Write which page you would find the entry word.

| page 23 **candle → card** | page 26 **common → conflict** | page 31 **corner → crawl** |

1. conceal _____

2. counter _____

3. captive _____

4. crane _____

5. confetti _____

6. carbon _____

7. compare _____

8. cover _____

9. count _____

10. canopy _____

Writing Practice: Write a descriptive paragraph about going on a safari in Africa.

Math Practice: Equivalent Numbers

Fill in the blanks with <, >, or =. Be careful and follow each sign. Then solve problem 5.

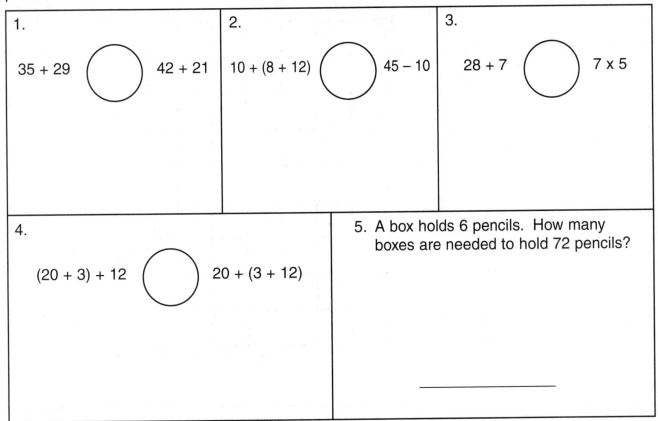

1.

35 + 29 ◯ 42 + 21

2.

10 + (8 + 12) ◯ 45 − 10

3.

28 + 7 ◯ 7 x 5

4.

(20 + 3) + 12 ◯ 20 + (3 + 12)

5. A box holds 6 pencils. How many boxes are needed to hold 72 pencils?

_____

Language Practice: Homonyms

Circle the correct word in each sentence.

1. We bought a (fir, fur) tree for our Christmas tree.
2. She carried a (pail, pale) of water to wash her car.
3. May we have (some, sum) soda with our pizza?
4. They played volleyball on the (beech, beach).
5. Mr. Jones (tied, tide) the knot in the rope.
6. My sister asked for a (peace, piece) of my birthday cake.
7. The (led, lead) in my pencil just broke.
8. Have you (seen, scene) the new television show?
9. What did Joann give you (four, for) your birthday?
10. I think Joshua ate (to, too, two) much candy.

Writing Practice: Think about something you've been studying in science. Write a paragraph about what you've learned.

Name _____

Math Practice: Mathematical Terms

Circle the correct term to the underlined part of each number sentence. Then solve problem 5.

1. <u>81</u> divided by 9 = 9
 	
  a. subtrahend
  b. addends
  c. multiplier
  d. dividend
	2. 6 x <u>6</u> = 36
	
	  a. subtrahend
	  b. addends
	  c. multiplier
	  d. dividend
		3. <u>33</u> − 11 = 22
		
		  a. subtrahend
		  b. addends
		  c. multiplier
		  d. dividend

4. <u>10 + 10</u> = 20
 	
  a. subtrahend
  b. addends
  c. multiplier
  d. dividend
	5. It takes 24 inches of string to wrap a package. How much string will be needed to wrap 25 packages?
	
	  _____	

Language Practice: Verb Usage

Circle the correct verb in each sentence.

1. The sun has (rise, rose, risen) brightly this morning.

2. The Founder's Day program has (begin, began, begun) late.

3. The swim team has (swim, swam, swum) five laps.

4. The walnuts have (fall, fell, fallen) off the trees.

5. Watermelon was (grow, grew, grown) on my uncle's farm.

6. My mother and I will (go, went, gone) to the basketball game tonight.

7. The window pane was (break, broke, broken) by a rock.

8. The principal has (tell, told, telled) us the announcements.

9. Where was Kate (hid, hide, hidden)?

10. The _Titanic_ was (sink, sank, sunk) many years ago.

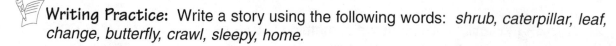

Writing Practice: Write a story using the following words: _shrub, caterpillar, leaf, change, butterfly, crawl, sleepy, home._

Name _____

Math Practice: Money

Solve each word problem using money.

1. Jerome spent between $12.00 and $13.00. Which two food items did he buy? a. steak $5.50 b. hot dog $2.75 c. shrimp $7.00 d. French fries $1.50	2. Lacey went to the bookstore for her teacher. The teacher gave her $1.00. Mrs. Woodson gave Lacey the following change: a quarter, 2 nickels, and 3 pennies. Which item did Lacey buy? a. pencil $0.25 b. notebook $0.62 c. eraser $0.10 d. ruler $0.68
3. The fourth grade hired a bus to take a trip to Mammoth Cave. It cost $15.00. Each student paid $0.50. How many students rode the bus? _____	4. The second graders collected money for charity. They collected 50 quarters, 65 dimes, 105 nickels, and 245 pennies. How much money did they collect? _____

Language Practice: Antonyms/Synonyms

If the words are antonyms, write **A** in the space. If the words are synonyms, write **S** in the space.

_____ 1. difficult/easy

_____ 2. brave/coward

_____ 3. empty/full

_____ 4. finish/end

_____ 5. residence/home

_____ 6. shouted/whispered

_____ 7. cent/penny

_____ 8. swift/slow

_____ 9. friend/foe

_____ 10. liberty/freedom

Writing Practice: It rains so hard one afternoon that your bus gets stuck in the mud. Write a story about the unusual bus ride.

Name _____

Math Practice: Mixed Computation

Solve each problem.

1. 906,370 3,912 + 658	2. 1.27 x 29	3. 6,175 − 967
4. 8)467	5. Bertha has 37 marbles. Her friend, Anthony has 41 marbles. They decide to put all the marbles together and then divide them up evenly. How many marbles would each person get? _____	

Language Practice: Nouns

Circle all words in the fish that are nouns.

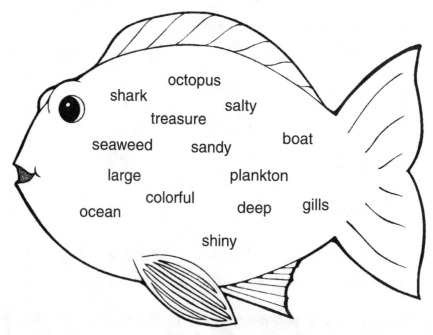

octopus
shark
salty
treasure
seaweed   sandy   boat
large   plankton
colorful
ocean   deep   gills
shiny

✎ **Writing Practice:** Write a story using eight of the words above.

Math Practice: Measurement

Fill in the blanks for problems 1–4. Then solve problem 5.

1. 1 quart is _____ pints.	2. There are _____ ounces in a pound.	3. 4 quarts make _____ gallon.
4. $\frac{1}{2}$ of a gallon is _____ quarts.	5. Stanley's father bought a car that weighed $\frac{1}{4}$ of a ton. How much did it weigh in pounds? _____	

Language Practice: Syllables

Circle the words that have a long vowel sound in the first syllable.

table	baby	bridle
money	apple	lucky
lady	nature	pizza
window	hero	pilot
robin	fatal	nickel
flower	drama	music

 Writing Practice: Some people like to be by themselves. Others don't like to be alone. Write a paragraph explaining which one you prefer.

Name _____

Math Practice: Probability

Solve the problems.

1. If Kareem and Susan play a game of basketball (one-on-one), what is the probability that Kareem will win? _____	2. If Bill is in a class of 30 students and his teacher is asking questions, what is the probability that the teacher will call on Bill to answer the question? _____	3. You have a jar full of marbles. There are 4 blue, 5 red, 3 yellow, 2 white, and 1 black. What is the probability of pulling out a blue marble? _____

4. Robin and Maya are playing a game. Mary needs 5 spaces to win. What is the probability that Maya will spin a 5 to win the game? _____	5. Donna rolled the die five times. Each time she rolled a four. What was the total amount she rolled altogether? _____

Language Practice: Commas

Write a **Y** if the sentence is written correctly with commas. Write an **N** if the sentence is not correct, then add commas where needed.

_____ 1. Yes you may go to see a movie with Sean.

_____ 2. "Math is fun," said Belle to Mr. Roberts.

_____ 3. I like pizza, hamburgers hotdogs, and French fries.

_____ 4. Our class saw lions tigers, and zebras at the zoo.

_____ 5. "I enjoyed my day today" said Mrs. Nobel.

_____ 6. Mom bought milk, eggs, and chicken at the store.

_____ 7. Do you have chores to do at your house Gretchen?

_____ 8. On Monday May 10 1955 someone famous was born.

_____ 9. She was born in Greenville, South Carolina.

_____10. Yesterday we played basketball football and soccer during P. E.

Writing Practice: What is some advice a parent has given you? How do you feel when you're given advice? Write a paragraph explaining your answer.

Math Practice: Estimation

Do not work each problem. Estimate the answers. Write it in the blank. Then solve problem 5.

1. Estimate to the nearest hundred. 436 + 157 _____	2. Estimate to the nearest hundred. 713 – 324 _____	3. Estimate to the nearest ten. 29 x 65 _____
4. Estimate to the nearest ten. $24\overline{)442}$ _____	5. Daphne had 75 tulip bulbs to plant. She planted 5 bulbs in a row. How many rows did she plant? _____	

Language Practice: Kind of Sentences

Fill in the blanks with the words: *declarative, interrogative, imperative,* or *exclamatory*.

1. Have you ever been on a farm? _____

2. You get to see all kinds of animals on a farm. _____

3. "I like pigs the best," said Leeann. _____

4. Don't step in the mud. _____

5. What a beautiful countryside! _____

6. Did you know that people work hard on a farm? _____

7. They grow many fruits and vegetables that we eat. _____

8. "I love fresh corn!" exclaimed Markel. _____

9. "Don't make a pig out of yourself," said Markel's mother. _____

10. May we come back and visit again? _____

Writing Practice: Write a persuasive paragraph to convince your teacher that you are serious about school.

Math Practice: Time

Write how many minutes are between the given times. Then solve problem 5.

1. 6:00 A.M. and 6:25 A.M. _____	2. 4:25 P.M. and 5:10 P.M. _____	3. 2:30 A.M. and 2:56 A.M. _____
4. 11:55 P.M. and 12:05 A.M. _____	5. Jan gets up at 7:20 A.M. She goes to school at 8:05 A.M. How much time does she have to get ready? _____ Her class comes back from lunch at 12:00. Is this A.M. or P.M.? _____	

Language Practice: Abbreviations

Choose the correct abbreviation of each state.

MA	ME	MN	MS	WA	WV
MD	MI	MO	MT	WI	WY

Maine   _____   Maryland   _____   Massachusetts _____

Michigan   _____   Minnesota   _____   Mississippi   _____

Missouri   _____   Montana   _____   Washington   _____

West Virginia _____   Wisconsin   _____   Wyoming   _____

 Writing Practice: If you could plan the ideal trip across the United States, where would you go and why?

Math Practice: Mixed Review

Write **T** if the statement is true, and **F** if the statement is false. Then solve problem 5.

1. The sum of 2, 4, 6, and 8 is 20. _____	2. 2 quarts is equal to 1 gallon. _____	3. There are 52 weeks in one year. _____
4. The product of 12 and 12 is 124. _____	5. If one penguin eats 80 kg of food per day, how many kg of food would it take to feed a penguin for a week? _____	

Language Practice: Addresses

Write these addresses correctly in the boxes below.

1. morris f. rogers
   11 spencer st
   lanark il 61046

2. monique B. robinson
   243 central ave
   new york ny 10028

 Writing Practice: Some people think we'll have robots in our homes in the future. Write a story about a robot that lives in your house.

Math Practice: Mixed Computation

Solve each problem.

1. 14,132 + 2,478	2. $60.00 − $13.95	3. $87.54 x 15

4.

$$7\overline{)231}$$

5. A camera store ordered 56 cameras. Each cost $68.00. What was the cost of the order?

_____

Language Practice: Consonant Blends

Write which sound the *ch* makes in each word. Choose from **k**, **ch**, or **sh**.

1. church _____

2. couch _____

3. choir _____

4. chandelier _____

5. chapter _____

6. chair _____

7. echo _____

8. aches _____

9. chef _____

10. school _____

11. chauffer _____

12. each _____

 Writing Practice: What is a friend? What makes a good friend? Do you have a special friend? Write a paragraph by answering these questions.

Math Practice: Time

Read the times and write A.M. or P.M.

1. 6:30 (sunrise) _____	2. 3:00 (day) _____	3. 8:30 (bedtime) _____

4. 1:00 (night) _____	5. It is 8:00 A.M. If 12 hours go by, is it 8:00 A.M. or P.M.? _____

Language Practice: Dictionary Skills

Read each definition for *back*. Decide which definition best fits each sentence. Write the letter of the correct definition in each blank.

a. part of a person opposite the face	c. related to the past
	d. at the rear
b. uppermost part of an animal	e. spine

_____ 1. Tyra hurt her back playing volleyball.

_____ 2. Jerrod was told to go to the back of the line.

_____ 3. Michael likes to pet his dog on his back.

_____ 4. Shannon turned around and went back to school.

_____ 5. I combed the back of my hair.

 Writing Practice: What part of the school day do you like the best? Write a paragraph telling about your favorite part of school.

Math Practice: Variables

Solve for *x*.

1. *x* = 17 + 5	2. *x* = 21 − 3	3. 6 multiplied by *x* = 54
x = _____	*x* = _____	*x* = _____

4. *x* divided by 8 = 8	5. A life jacket is needed for each tourist on 8 tour boats. How many life jackets are needed if each tour boat holds 185 passengers?
x = _____	_____

Language Practice: Main Idea

Read each group of words. Write the main idea on the blank.

1. banana, papaya, orange, grapefruit, grape

   _____

2. singing carols, shopping, wrapping gifts, decorating a tree, snow

   _____

3. goal, net, referee, kicking, black and white ball

   _____

4. guide words, definitions, pronunciation, parts of speech, spelling

   _____

Now write a list of 5 words or phrases that go with each category.

5. Thanksgiving things

   _____

6. things at a circus

   _____

 Writing Practice: Look at the one of the lists above. Write a story, beginning with the main idea, and then finish the story by writing sentences with the list of words or phrases. Remember, stories have a beginning, a middle, and an end.

Name _____

Math Practice: Estimation

Estimate to find each answer.

1. Tree 1 = 564 ft. Tree 2 = 230 ft. The first tree is about _____ feet taller than the second tree. a. 500 ft. b. 200 ft. c. 300 ft.	2. Top of house = 127 ft. Tree = 61 ft. The top of the house is about _____ feet taller than the tree. a. 60 ft. b. 100 ft. c. 200 ft.	3. What do you think you could do in 10 seconds? a. tie your shoes b. count to 100 c. write an essay
4. How many times do you think you could hop on one foot? a. 50 times b. 500 times c. 5,000 times	5. An average of 65 people walked through the stamp exhibit every hour. How many people visited the exhibit during the 12 hours it was open? _____	

Language Practice: Plurals

Sometimes an *s* or *es* is added to words to make them plural. Some words do not follow this rule. Write the plural of these words.

1. antenna _____

2. axis _____

3. foot _____

4. elf _____

5. deer _____

6. mouse _____

7. child _____

8. goose _____

9. larva _____

10. 5 _____

 Writing Practice: Write a story about being a hero. What happened, and what heroic thing did you do?

Math Practice: Addition and Average

Add the scores of each bowler. Write the bowler who had the highest total of pins. Then solve problem 5.

1. Jeb's Scores	2. Parth's Scores	3. Micah's Scores
120	132	90
114	98	144
105	111	122
Total = _____	Total = _____	Total = _____

4. Who was the winner?	5. Kevin bowled 3 games in a tournament. What is the average of his score?
_____	(see table below)

5. Kevin bowled 3 games in a tournament. What is the average of his score?

Game	Score
1	158
2	172
3	211

Average = _____

Language Practice: Capitalization

Circle the words that should be capitalized.

1. i live on bryan street.

2. i have lived there since last february.

3. we moved in our new house on a saturday.

4. we used to live near salt lake city.

5. i was born in chicago on january 10.

6. on my birthday i am going to see niagra falls.

7. my mother speaks spanish.

8. she was born in mexico.

 Writing Practice: Write a paragraph about a favorite book or story. Describe why it is your favorite.

Name _____

Math Practice: Fractions

Solve each problem. Reduce to lowest terms.

1. $2\frac{2}{9} + 4\frac{7}{9} =$ _____	2. $12\frac{4}{16} - 8\frac{3}{16} =$ _____	3. $32\frac{4}{7} + 4\frac{5}{7} =$ _____

4. $8\frac{8}{9} - 5\frac{6}{9} =$ _____	5. Kim Ling had 41 marbles. Her friend had 28. Kim gave her friend some of her marbles. Now Kim has 29. How many did Kim give her friend? _____ How many does her friend have now? _____

Language Practice: Alphabetical Order

Write the following groups of words in alphabetical order.

1. ensign   _____

   engine   _____

   envelope   _____

   enamel   _____

   enormous   _____

   enchant   _____

   enjoy   _____

2. grass   _____

   grammar   _____

   grassy   _____

   gray   _____

   grab   _____

   gravel   _____

   grade   _____

 Writing Practice: What fun thing (or things) did you do this past weekend? Write about your adventures.

Math Practice: Mixed Review

Solve each problem.

1. Write the word name for the number below. 372,432.03 _____ _____ _____	2. Put the numerals in order from least to greatest. 365,321 _____ 3,653.21 _____ 36,532.1 _____ 365.321 _____	3. $14.8 - 8.56 =$ _____
4. $8.64 + 13.4 + 2.59 =$ _____	5. Your teacher wanted you to divide all these numbers by the same number, and the answers would all come out even. The numbers are 24, 68, 104, and 80. What number can you divide into all four numbers? _____	

Language Practice: Adverbs

Circle the adverb in each sentence.

1. Janet plays the flute well.

2. Harold ran quickly to the game.

3. She spoke softly to her dog.

4. He is a very good reader.

5. The moon shone brightly over the water.

6. The police officer handles his gun carefully.

7. She wisely completed all of her homework.

 Writing Practice: Do you have a favorite song? Write what your favorite song is and tell why it is your favorite.

Math Practice: Money

Look at the menu. Four families from the neighborhood ordered fast food one evening. Compute the cost of each family's meal, using the menu.

1. Family 1 ordered 2 hot dogs, 2 French fries, 1 potato salad, and 2 sodas. Total = _____	2. Family 2 ordered 1 hamburger, 3 pizzas, 1 milkshake, and 3 sodas. Total = _____	3. Family 3 ordered 2 corn dogs, 1 pizza, 2 potato chips, and 3 milkshakes. Total = _____

4. Family 4 ordered 1 of each item on the menu. Total = _____	**Fast Food Menu** hot dog $1.25 hamburger $1.50 pizza $1.50 corn dog $1.25 French fries $1.00 potato salad $0.90 potato chips $0.75 soft drink $0.50 milkshake $1.15 ice cream cone $0.80

Language Practice: Pronouns

Write the pronoun above the underlined word.

1. Marques ran fast. <u>Marques</u> won the race.

2. The boys like to play baseball. <u>The boys</u> play it every Saturday.

3. Mom went to the grocery store. <u>Mom</u> bought food for our lunches.

4. Barbara and I are friends. <u>Barbara and I</u> like to talk on the phone.

Circle the possessive pronoun in each sentence.

5. "That's my book," said Emily.

6. Did the baby play with her ball?

7. The blue backpack is mine.

8. The dog ate its bone.

Writing Practice: Write a paragraph using the sentence starter below.

The art of being friendly . . .

Name _____

Math Practice: Decimals

Add each group of numbers with decimals. Then solve problem 5.

1. 15,873 + 5.32 = _____	2. 15.873 + 53.2 = _____	3. 1,587.3 + .532 = _____
4. 1.5873 + 532 = _____		5. There are 24 hours in one day. How many hours are there in one week? _____ How many hours are in 12 weeks? _____

Language Practice: Predicate

Choose the correct verb for each sentence.

1. _____ the students play kickball. (Let, Leave)

2. Please don't _____ on the floor. (sit, set)

3. We _____ our bird to talk. (taught, learned)

4. Where _____ you yesterday? (was, were)

5. There _____ two bikes in the yard. (is, are)

6. Where have you _____ my picture? (took, taken)

7. We _____ our lunch in our classroom. (ate, eaten)

8. _____ I go to the mall with you? (may, can)

Writing Practice: Write a paragraph using the sentence starter below.

I have some good memories about . . .

Math Practice: Multiplication

Solve each problem.

1. 974 x 63	2. 290 x 76	3. 794 x 13
4. 69 x 42	5. Jenny bought a car for $17,936.29. Miguel bought a car for $25,000.00. How much more did Miguel spend than Jenny? _____	

Language Practice: Adjectives

Fill in the blanks with an adjective.

1. I saw a _____ cat running down the street.

2. We like to eat _____ candy.

3. I read _____ books last month.

4. The lady has _____ children.

5. We sat on a _____ couch.

6. We ate a _____ cake for dessert.

7. Mom baked _____ cookies for my party.

8. My _____ doll was broken.

Writing Practice: Pretend you are an astronaut. Write about your adventures in space.

Math Practice: Subtraction

Subtract the number at the top from each number listed below. Then solve problem 5.

1. subtract 32	2. subtract 21	3. subtract 19

1.		2.		3.	
44		67		48	
58		42		39	
63		29		27	
33		90		19	

4. subtract 8

91	
87	
73	
60	

5. California has about 65 times more pets than the state of Georgia. If Georgia has 283,000 pets, how many does California have?

_____

Language Practice: Prefixes

Write what each word means by looking at the meanings of the following prefixes.

uni = one	*tri* = three	*inter* = between	*pre* = before
bi = two	*semi* = half	*intra* = within	*sub* = under

1. unicycle _____

2. bicentennial _____

3. triangle _____

4. semicircle _____

5. interstate _____

6. intravenous _____

7. prepay_____

8. subway _____

 Writing Practice: Write a newspaper article for your school newspaper convincing students and teachers to recycle.

Math Practice: Money

You've just inherited one million dollars, but there's one catch. You have to spend all of it or you lose it. Answer the questions. Choose from the items listed in the box below.

1. List the 4 items that you would buy.	2. What is the total cost of all 4 items?	3. How much money do you have left?
_____ _____ _____ _____	_____	_____

house	$250,000.00	**ten-speed bicycle**	$250.00
sports car	$25,000.00	**trip to Disney World**	$1,200.00
swimming pool	$15,000.00	**fast-food restaurant**	$56,000.00
boat	$31,000.00	**roller skating rink**	$100,000.00

Language Practice: Suffixes

Write what each word means by looking at the meanings of the following suffixes.

(-er) one who does something	*(-ee)* one who receives something	*(-meter)* device for measuring
(-ation) act of	*(-less)* without	*(-y)* having
(-ous) having	*(-ful)* full of	

1. teacher _____

2. thermometer _____

3. employee _____

4. transportation _____

5. careless _____

6. chilly _____

7. joyous _____

8. beautiful _____

Writing Practice: Write a paragraph using the sentence starter below.

One of the strangest sights I ever saw was . . .

Math Practice: Money

Count the total change. Write it on the blank provided.

1. _____	2. _____	3. _____
3 dollars 3 half dollars 3 quarters 3 dimes 3 nickels 3 pennies	2 quarters 12 dimes 5 nickels 24 pennies	12 dollars 4 quarters 2 dimes

4. _____	5. Terell saved 12 quarters, 6 dimes, 14 nickels, and 13 pennies. Shamika saved 10 quarters, 8 dimes, 12 nickels, and 20 pennies. Who saved the most money?
5 dollars 5 quarters 5 nickels 5 pennies	_____

Language Practice: Dictionary Skills

Look up these words to find their origin.

1. parrot

_____

2. raccoon

_____

3. chocolate

_____

4. automobile

_____

5. piano

_____

6. chimpanzee

_____

7. pajamas

_____

8. tea

_____

9. pretzel

_____

10. cookie

_____

 Writing Practice: A *fable* is a story that teaches a lesson, and animals are usually the characters. Write your own fable about a chicken and a cow.

Math Practice: Fractions

Solve each problem.

1. $\frac{3}{8} + \frac{2}{8} + \frac{1}{8} =$ _____	2. $\frac{11}{12} - \frac{9}{12} =$ _____	3. $\frac{20}{25} - \frac{4}{5} =$ _____

4.

$12\frac{2}{9} + 7\frac{4}{18} =$ _____

5. Amy walked $\frac{2}{10}$ of a mile to the park. Johnson walked $\frac{7}{10}$ of a mile to the park.

How many total miles did they walk?

_____

Who walked the farthest?

_____

Language Practice: Vocabulary

Write a word from the word bank.

Word Bank

breezy	blossom	shamrock	air
spring	kite	pot-of-gold	lamb

1. a flower

_____

2. windy

_____

3. a clover

_____

4. at the end of a rainbow

_____

5. season after winter

_____

6. farm animal

_____

7. atmosphere

_____

8. child's toy

_____

Writing Practice: Write a descriptive paragraph about spending the day at the beach.

Name _____

Math Practice: Measurement

Solve each problem.

1. About how long is a crayon? 3 in. or 3 ft.	2. About how much does a large bucket hold? 5 pt. or 5 gal.	3. Which is used to measure milk in a glass? cup or pint
4. About how long is a straw? 5 cm or 5.2 km	5. What was the total distance of a race if it had 4 laps, each 1,125 meters long? _____	

Language Practice: Nouns, Verbs, and Adjectives

Write words that begin with the letter at the top of each chart.

	m
noun	
verb	
adjective	

	a
noun	
verb	
adjective	

	l
noun	
verb	
adjective	

	s
noun	
verb	
adjective	

	r
noun	
verb	
adjective	

	w
noun	
verb	
adjective	

Writing Practice: If you could give your teacher a suggestion, what would it be?

Name _____

Math Practice: Mixed Computation

Solve each problem.

1.	2.	3.
482 658 + 217	3,040 − 1,829	$87.54 x 72

4.	5. A farmer has 43 cattle. 19 are sold. He then buys 22 more. How many cattle does he have now?
6) 2,516	_____

Language Practice: Dictionary Skills

Which word has the same sound? Circle the answer.

1. needle: a. let   b. ceiling   c. eight   4. August: a. out   b. brown   c. jaw

2. lean: a. better b. best   c. sneeze   5. fair: a. plane b. mare   c. clean

3. claw: a. boat   b. bought   c. clay

Circle the vowel sound that completes the word.

6. a person in a circus: cl___n
   a. ou   b. aw   c. ow

7. head of indian tribe: ch___f
   a. ie   b. ei   c. ee

8. what the pig built his house of: str___
   a. ay   b. aw   c. ew

9. a sandwich is made of: br___d
   a. ai   b. ea   c. ei

10. a trip on a ship: cr___se
   a. oo   b. ou   c. ui

Writing Practice: Write a paragraph describing your Mondays.

Math Practice: Reading a Graph

Answer the questions about the circle graph.

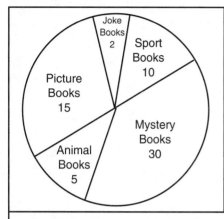

1. How many students checked out books altogether?

_____

2. Which type of book is checked out twice as much as picture books?

_____

3. How many more students checked out mystery books than animal books?

_____

4. What is the least popular book?

_____

Which type of book is checked out the most?

_____

Language Practice: Fact or Opinion

Write **F** if the statement is fact and **O** if the statement is opinion.

_____ 1. Rabbits are furry animals.

_____ 2. Spiders are ugly.

_____ 3. Basketball is easier to play than baseball.

_____ 4. My dad is 6' 3" tall.

_____ 5. Squash tastes terrible!

_____ 6. Lansing is the capital of Michigan.

_____ 7. Fish breathe through gills.

_____ 8. You shouldn't watch too much television.

 Writing Practice: Write about what you think it would be like to live in Alaska during the season when it's dark 24 hours a day.

Name _____

Math Practice: Addition

Write corresponding numbers to the alphabet under each letter. (Example: A = 1, B = 2, C = 3, etc.) Add up the numbers in these words. Then solve problem 5.

1. paper _____	2. glue _____	3. pencil _____
4. notebook _____	5. Which word added up was the largest number? _____	

Language Practice: Following Directions

Follow the steps. Begin by putting your pencil on the center square. Circle each letter you stop at. Write it in the space provided.

1. Go 1 block West
2. Go 2 blocks North
3. Go 3 blocks East
4. Go 4 blocks South
5. Go 1 block West
6. Go 4 blocks North
7. Go 1 block West

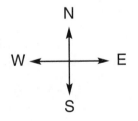

E	R	S	D	I
T	P	A	H	A
K	F	★	M	B
Q	C	G	L	D
S	K	J	N	E

What do all people need? ____ ____ ____ ____ ____ ____ ____

 Writing Practice: If you had x-ray vision, what would you use it for? Write a paragraph telling about this special gift.

Math Practice: Variables

Find the value of *x*. Then solve problem 5.

1. 23 + *x* = 31	2. 17 − *x* = 12	3. *x* = 3 x 4
x = _____	*x* = _____	*x* = _____

4. *x* = 43 ÷ 3	5. LaToya went to bed at 9:36 P.M. She woke up 23 minutes later to get a drink of water. What time did she wake up?
x = _____	_____

Language Practice: Spelling

Begin with the word, look at the clues, and change one letter each time to make a new word.

1. whole

   _ _ _ _ _ : mammal

   _ _ _ _ _ : rock

   _ _ _ _ _ : measures weight

   _ _ _ _ _ : frighten

2. plane

   _ _ _ _ _ : grows in the ground

   _ _ _ _ _ : diagonal

   _ _ _ _ _ : informal speech

   _ _ _ _ _ : bandage for arm

3. grab

   _ _ _ _ : dreary

   _ _ _ _ : heavy freight wagon

   _ _ _ _ : talk to God

   _ _ _ _ : hunted for food

 Writing Practice: Write a paragraph to complete this idea.

If I were three inches tall, I would . . .

Math Practice: Mixed Computation

Solve each problem.

1.	2.	3. Which of these symbols should go in the box to get the smallest answer?
43 x 28	181 x 22	100 ☐ 20 = a. + c. x b. − d. ÷

4. Which one would show the largest answer? a. + c. x b. − d. ÷	5. Marilynn has 5 pencils, Alfred has 7 pencils, Jasmine has 8 pencils, and Ryan has 2 pencils. How many pencils do they all have together? _____ How many more pencils does Marilynn and Alfred have than Jasmine and Ryan? _____

Language Practice: Subject

Find the subject in this mixed-up sentence. Circle the subject.

1. Down the street came Felipe.

2. Across the room sat Ned.

3. Under the table was her nickel.

4. Over the hill ran a deer.

5. On the floor was his shoes.

6. Into the classroom came the teacher.

7. Through the woods scampered a rabbit.

8. Around the corner came a barking dog.

 Writing Practice: You've just found an old bottle. You clean it up and . . . Poof! A genie appears. What three wishes will you make?

Math Practice: Reading a Graph

Answer each question about the graph.

1. Which activity is enjoyed the most? _____	2. How many more people go on vacation than go to camp? _____	3. Which activities have the same number of people? _____ _____

4. Which activity is enjoyed the least? _____	**Things to Do During Summer**

Things to Do During Summer

swim
vacation
play outside
sleep late
go to camp

2 4 6 8 10 12 14 16

Language Practice: Kinds of Sentences

Label each sentence with the correct letter.

_____ 1. Are you going today?

_____ 2. You are going today.

_____ 3. Where are you going today?

_____ 4. Please go today.

_____ 5. We're going today!

_____ 6. We're going today?

_____ 7. We're going today.

_____ 8. You need to go right now!

a. declarative
b. interrogative
c. imperative
d. exclamatory

 Writing Practice: What do you think your pencil would say if it could talk? Write a story about what your pencil would say.

Math Practice: Roman Numerals

Write the number that each Roman numeral stands for. Then solve problem 5.

1. XXXVI	2. XLIV	3. LV
_____	_____	_____

4. CLIII	5. Bill went to buy a video game at the toy store. It cost $50.00, but he only had $32.76. How much more money did he need?
_____	_____

Language Practice: Dictionary Skills

Use your dictionary to find the meanings of the words below.

1. divan _____

2. artichoke _____

3. kilt _____

4. chemise _____

5. ottoman _____

6. emblem _____

7. legume _____

8. pew _____

9. asparagus _____

Writing Practice: Write a paragraph using the sentence starter below.

The class wouldn't be quiet, so . . .

Math Practice: Time

Write how many hours are between the times given. Then solve problem 5.

1. 2:00 P.M. and 10:00 P.M.	2. 6:00 A.M. and 1:00 P.M.	3. 1:18 A.M. and 10:18 P.M.
_____	_____	_____

4. 12:00 P.M. and 12:00 A.M.	5. Mehul called his friend Jim at 2:23 P.M. to come over and work on their school project. If they met at 6:30 P.M., how long would it be before they began working?
_____	_____

Language Practice: Prefix

Match the correct **en** prefix word with its definition.

_____ 1. get pleasure from   a. enslave

_____ 2. commit   b. engage

_____ 3. wrap   c. entrap

_____ 4. put name on a list   d. enjoy

_____ 5. make a slave of   e. enfold

_____ 6. on the way   f. enliven

_____ 7. make lively   g. enroll

_____ 8. catch   h. enroute

Writing Practice: Write a paragraph using the sentence starter below.

Everyone in the room started to laugh when . . .

Math Practice: Mathematical Terms

Circle the correct mathematical term for the underlined numbers. Then solve problem 5.

1. 10 − 8 = <u>2</u> a. product b. sum c. difference d. quotient	2. 23 + 23 = <u>46</u> a. product b. sum c. difference d. quotient	3. 20 ÷ 5 = <u>4</u> a. product b. sum c. difference d. quotient
4. 3 x 5 = <u>15</u> a. product b. sum c. difference d. quotient	5. Cleveland had 104,238 in population, Columbus has 679,234 in population, and Dayton has 414,757 in population. What is the total population of all three cities? _____	

Language Practice: Homonyms

Eight homonyms are used incorrectly in this story. Circle each of them and write the correct word in the blanks below.

> It was a beautiful blew sky. We were playing football with hour friends. Stephan through the ball at me. It wood have dropped, but I fell forward to get it. Suddenly, I screamed! I had fallen on a be. I ran home sew hard my feat began to hurt. Later that knight, I went to bed with my leg hurting from the bee sting.

_____, _____, _____, _____,

_____, _____, _____, _____

 Writing Practice: Write a story using the sentence starter below.

We heard a "thump" outside the window . . .

Math Practice: Place Value

For problems 1–4, name the place value in the following number: 1,876,321.
Then solve problem 5.

1. What is the place value of the 7? **1,876,321** _____	2. What is the place value of the 6? **1,876,321** _____	3. What is the place value of the 3? **1,876,321** _____
4. What is the place value of the 8? **1,876,321** _____	5. If three students paid $2.35 for lunch and four students paid $1.85 for lunch, how much did all the lunches cost? _____	

Language Practice: Prepositions

Fill in the blanks with a preposition from the box below. Use each word only once.

toward	before	to	into
with	down	around	from

1. I walked to school _____ my sister.

2. We went _____ the corner and _____ the street.

3. As we walked _____ the school, the bell rang.

4. My teacher walked _____ me and said, "Get a note _____ the office."

5. They gave me a note, and I went _____ my class _____ the second bell.

Writing Practice: Write a story using the sentence starter below.

The whole school could hear Matilda screaming . . .

Math Practice: Rounding

Round to the nearest whole number. Then solve problem 5.

1. 4.3 = _____	2. 9.78 = _____	3. 85.03 = _____
4. 7.1 = _____	5. Merlin walked 2.3 miles, Arnold walked 7.5 miles, William walked 3.1 miles, and Franklin walked 8.7 miles. Round each to the nearest whole number. How many miles did they walk in all? _____	

Language Practice: Verb

Fill in the chart with the correct form of the verb.

Present	Past	Past Participle
sing		sung
	rang	rung
read	read	
think		thought
	walked	walked
take		taken
sit	sat	
blow		blown

Writing Practice: Write a story using the sentence starter below.

In the middle of the night, I was thirsty. When I got up, I couldn't believe my eyes . . .

Name _____

Math Practice: Reading a Chart

Answer the questions about these mountain ranges.

Mountains in Feet	
Mont Blanc	15,771
Mount Kilimanjaro	19,340
Mount McKinley	20,320
Aconcagua	22,834
Mount Everest	29,028

1. Which mountain has the highest peak?

_____

2. How much higher is Aconcagua than Mount McKinley?

_____

3. Which mountain has the lowest peak?

_____

4. In the list above, what is the difference between the highest and lowest peaks?

_____

Language Practice: Handwriting

Write the names of the 13 original colonies in your best handwriting.

New Hampshire _____   North Carolina _____

Delaware _____   Connecticut _____

Massachusetts _____   South Carolina _____

Maryland _____   Pennsylvania _____

New York _____   Georgia _____

Virginia _____   New Jersey _____

Rhode Island _____

 Writing Practice: There is a poem called "The Purple Cow." Write a poem with another colored animal.

Math Practice: Fractions

Write each problem as a fraction. Then solve problem 5.

1. .15 = _____	2. 3.6 = _____	3. 7.52 = _____
4. 1.07 = _____	5. There were 15 yards of material bought to make curtains for the school play. The total cost was $135.00. How much did each yard of material cost? _____	

Language Practice: Antonym

Write an antonym for each word.

1. above _____

2. add _____

3. easy _____

4. leave _____

5. happy _____

6. heavy _____

7. many _____

8. brave _____

9. large _____

10. up _____

11. fat _____

12. long _____

13. clean _____

14. hard _____

15. shiny _____

16. wet _____

 Writing Practice: If you were a talk show host, what two guests would you invite to be on your show? What two questions would you ask them?

Math Practice: Mixed Computation

Solve the problems.

1. $\begin{array}{r} 3{,}261 \\ +\ 1{,}879 \\ \hline \end{array}$	2. $\begin{array}{r} 3{,}261 \\ -\ 1{,}879 \\ \hline \end{array}$	3. $\begin{array}{r} 3{,}261 \\ \times\quad 9 \\ \hline \end{array}$

4.

$9\overline{)3{,}261}$

5. Sammy went to the store. He bought 35 apples. They cost 9 cents each. How much did he spend?

_____

Language Practice: Sequencing

Rewrite the following paragraph in sequence. Then circle the key words that show sequencing.

Finally, put both slices together and enjoy! Then get out the peanut butter and jelly. Afterwards, spread jelly on the other slice of bread. Next, spread peanut butter on one slice of bread. To make a peanut butter and jelly sandwich, you first need two slices of bread.

_____

_____

_____

_____

Writing Practice: Write a paragraph about "How To Make a Grilled Cheese Sandwich."

Name _____

Math Practice: Geometry

Find the perimeter.

1.

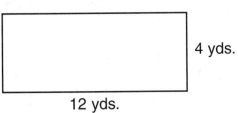

2 in.

4 in.

P = _____

2.

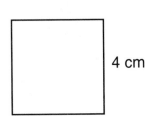

4 cm

P = _____

3.

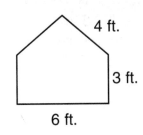

4 ft.

3 ft.

6 ft.

P = _____

4.

4 yds.

12 yds.

P = _____

5. If Jo weighs 50 pounds and Jill weighs 42 pounds, how much more does Jo weigh than Jill? _____

How much do they both weigh in all?

_____

Language Practice: Proofreading

Rewrite this paragraph correctly.

> Wellcome to the villege of harbor Town, Each cotage, shop and warehouse looks just like it did in the 1800s? Take a carriage ride alonge the eeege of the Harbor. youll love this special plase

_____

_____

_____

_____

_____

_____

Writing Practice: What is the most important thing you've ever learned? Write a paragraph and share it with a friend.

Math Practice: Points on a Grid

Write the coordinate pair for each point on the grid.

1. What is the ordered pair for *A*? _____	2. What is the ordered pair for *B*? _____	3. What is the ordered pair for *C*? _____

4. What is the ordered pair for *D*?

_____

Language Practice: Noun/Verb

Write **N** if the word is a noun. Write **V** if the word is a verb.

_____	1.	sing	_____ 9.	traveller
_____	2.	song	_____ 10.	travel
_____	3.	greeting	_____ 11.	erase
_____	4.	greet	_____ 12.	eraser
_____	5.	collect	_____ 13.	measurement
_____	6.	collection	_____ 14.	measure
_____	7.	freeze	_____ 15.	see
_____	8.	freezer	_____ 16.	sea

 Writing Practice: Predict the first day you think it will snow. Now write a paragraph to persuade me that you can have fun in the snow.

Name _____

Math Practice: Addition/Subtraction

Subtract and then check by addition. Then solve problem 5.

1. 423 − 187	2. 804 − 355	3. 1,201 − 987

4. 4,000 − 1,284	5. The sports store is having a 50% off sale. If T-shirts cost $8.00, shorts cost $5.00, and tennis shoes cost $24.00, how much will each item be at 50% off?

Language Practice: Verb

Replace each underlined verb with a more vivid verb.

1. Mom made a cake. _____

2. Steven made a race car. _____

3. I went to the store. _____

4. Dad went next door. _____

5. The girl came to school. _____

6. He came to the party. _____

Writing Practice: Write a paragraph using the sentence starter below.

One of the best things I can do is . . .

Name _____

Math Practice: Writing Numbers

Write the following number words in numbers. Then solve problem 5.

1. eight million, two thousand, five hundred sixty-two _____	2. three million, four hundred thousand, seven hundred thirty _____	3. sixty-four million, four hundred twenty-one thousand, three hundred seven _____
4. seventy-seven thousand, seven _____	5. We walked $\frac{1}{10}$ of a mile to see the giraffe, $\frac{2}{10}$ of a mile to see the elephants, $\frac{4}{10}$ of a mile to see the bears, and $\frac{1}{10}$ of a mile to see the tigers. How far did we walk? _____	

Language Practice: Literal/Figurative Language

Write **L** if the statement is literal and **F** if the statement is figurative.

_____ 1. I'm so hungry I could eat a horse!

_____ 2. I'm exhausted!

_____ 3. Darkness swallowed the ghost town.

_____ 4. Boy, I'm late. Time surely does fly.

_____ 5. The flower floated on the water.

_____ 6. His eyes burned with fire.

Writing Practice: Write a descriptive paragraph about spending the day at the zoo.

Name _____

Math Practice: Multiplication and Division

Solve each problem.

1.   234
      x 91
	2. 6,124
	      x 52
		3. 6)763

4. 3)12,982	5. Dad needed to buy four tires for the car. He could buy them for $28.99 each or four for $108.00. Which way would cost the least? _____

Language Practice: Figurative Language

Match the statement with the correct kind of figurative language.

_____ 1. He's fast as lightening!   a. personification

_____ 2. He's a pig!   b. simile

_____ 3. The tree wanted to rest.   c. alliteration

_____ 4. The wind blew with a whoosh!   d. metaphor

_____ 5. She sings the song sweetly.   e. onomatopoeia

 Writing Practice: You've just been given a pen pal. Write a letter to your pen pal describing yourself and telling him or her about yourself.

Name _____

Math Practice: Geometry

Name the lines. Write *parallel*, *intersecting*, or *perpendicular*. Then solve problem 5.

1. _____	2. _____	3. _____

4. _____	5. At the store, you spent $4.32. You give the cashier $10.02. How much money should you get back? _____

Language Practice: Pronouns

Write **I** or **me** in each blank.

1. _____ danced at the party.

2. She gave her CD to _____.

3. My sister and _____ are going shopping.

4. My cousin is going with Michiko and _____.

5. They gave _____ an award for attendance.

6. Sukey and _____ won a talent contest.

✎ **Writing Practice:** Write a paragraph about winning a contest.

Math Practice: Reading a Graph

Answer the questions about the graph below.

1. How many fish did Robert catch? _____	2. How many fish were caught altogether? _____	3. Who caught the same number of fish? _____

4. How many more fish did Jalisa catch than Ashley? _____	(graph)

Name	Number of Fish
Robert	🐟 🐟 🐟
Ashley	🐟
J. J.	🐟 🐟
Jalisa	🐟 🐟 🐟 🐟 🐟
Dixie	🐟 🐟

🐟 = 3 fish

Language Practice: Proofreading

Rewrite the sentences correctly.

1. scotts father said the month of march is finalle here

   _____

2. the white house is in washington dc

   _____

3. Janessa alway smiles and she seem happy

   _____

4. will she helps uus chek our homework?

   _____

5. my Friend is leaveing next weak

   _____

6. his mother weights for him and he wants to sea her

   _____

 Writing Practice: Write a paragraph about why you think we need our circulatory system.

Math Practice: Geometry

Write what type of angle—*right*, *acute*, or *obtuse*—is being used. Then solve problem 5.

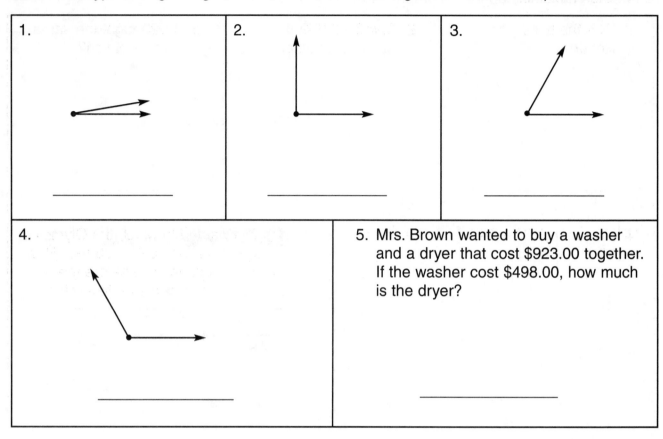

5. Mrs. Brown wanted to buy a washer and a dryer that cost $923.00 together. If the washer cost $498.00, how much is the dryer?

Language Practice: Adjectives

Write the correct adjective in each blank. Choose between *this, that, these,* and *those*.

1. We like _____ new clothes best.

2. Do you have any of _____ blue gel pens?

3. Surely _____ kind of safety program is best.

4. _____ math problem is very hard.

5. I wore _____ old shoes to school.

6. We saw _____ movies last summer.

7. _____ kind of book interests me.

8. Al likes _____ cars.

 Writing Practice: National Book Week is in November. Tell about a book you have read recently. What did you like about it? What did you dislike about it? Then illustrate a scene in the book.

Math Practice: Mixed Computation

Solve the problems.

1. 7,245 ÷ 6 =	2. 8,042 − 2,679 =	3. 1,023 x 42 =

4. 23 + 46 + 179 + 245 =	5. Johnnie wanted to watch the Olympics at 7:00 P.M. It was only 2:23 P.M. How much time did he have before the Olympics would come on television?

Language Practice: Prepositions

Find these prepositions in the puzzle.

after
among
beside
between
by
for
from
in
to
with

q	a	a	h	e	l	e	a	p	a	p
n	s	v	i	d	l	u	d	r	e	o
x	z	h	t	i	w	r	i	p	j	i
c	v	b	n	s	m	s	f	g	p	u
n	a	f	t	e	r	d	b	h	l	i
f	m	m	j	b	e	t	w	e	e	n
b	o	f	h	f	y	l	w	t	y	y
v	n	r	g	d	u	o	r	k	u	t
c	g	o	t	s	a	q	e	h	g	r
x	z	m	g	f	d	r	s	a	w	e

 Writing Practice: If you could be in either the summer or winter Olympics, which one would you choose? What would you do, and why?

Math Practice: Decimals

Add. Then solve problem 5.

1. 2.9461 + 56.03 =	2. 294.61 + 560.3 =	3. 2,946.1 + 5,603 =
_____	_____	_____

4. 29.461 + 5.603 =	5. The Hundred Years War was fought from 1337 to 1453. How many total years did the war go on?
_____	_____

Language Practice: Main Idea

Circle the topic that doesn't belong under the main idea. For problem 4, write four topics under the main idea.

1. Animals in the zoo
   a. bears
   b. dogs
   c. tigers
   d. monkeys

2. Favorite hobbies
   a. stamp collecting
   b. collecting dolls
   c. reading books
   d. doing homework

3. Why school is important
   a. learn how to clean your room
   b. learn new things
   c. learn to use the library
   d. learn to get along with others

4. You can learn a lot in social studies.
   a. _____
   b. _____
   c. _____
   d. _____

 Writing Practice: Write a story with the writing starter below.

It was a wonderful surprise . . .

Math Practice: Measurement

Circle which method of measurement would be more appropriate. Then solve problem 5.

1. width of your math book ruler or yardstick	2. length of your classroom ruler or yardstick	3. height of your teacher ruler or yardstick
4. length of your arm ruler or yardstick	5. Sammy gave Antonio six apples, Samantha three apples, and Kershawn five apples. If he started with 35 apples, how many does he have left? _____	

Language Practice: Spelling

Unscramble these words having to do with Christmas.

1. aittesnoip _____   6. shlgei _____

2. bbrion _____   7. lloyh _____

3. cdar _____   8. rewaht _____

4. kingcots _____   9. lorac _____

5. glena _____   10. repnest _____

 Writing Practice: Write a Christmas story using six of the words above.

Math Practice: Reading a Graph

Answer the questions about the graph.

1. On which days were 3 students absent? _____ _____	2. Which day had the most students absent? _____	3. Were more students absent on Wednesday or Thursday? _____

4. How many more students were absent on Tuesday than Wednesday?

_____

Number of Students Absent

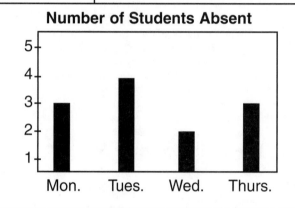

Language Practice: Direct Object

Circle the direct object in each sentence.

1. Sancho threw the football to Jim.

2. Mom ate popcorn after supper.

3. Harriet Tubman led slaves to freedom.

4. The children smelled the bright flowers.

5. Ed played the trumpet in band class.

 Writing Practice: Write a story using the sentence starter below.

I was in a haunted house . . .

Math Practice: Writing Numbers

For problems 1 and 2, write the words in numbers. For problems 3 and 4, write the numbers in words. Then solve problem 5.

1. six million, one hundred four thousand, two hundred fifty-five _____	2. two hundred seventy-two thousand, six hundred ninety _____	3. 13,765 _____ _____ _____ _____
4. 1,206,400 _____ _____ _____	5. You and three friends are buying a present for your teacher and will need to pay equal amounts. The total is $20.44. How much will each pay? _____	

Language Practice: Story Comprehension

Answer the questions about the story.

> Amelia Earhart is known for being the first woman pilot to fly across the Atlantic Ocean. She made this famous flight in 1932. She received an award after this famous flight. The award was the Distinguished Flying Cross, and she was the first woman to have received the award. In 1937, she began a flight that would take her around the world. Her plane disappeared over the Pacific Ocean, and to this day, no one knows what happened to her.

1. What did Amelia Earhart do in 1932? _____

2. Name the award she received? _____

3. What did Amelia Earhart attempt to do in 1937? _____

4. How did she die? _____

 Writing Practice: Write what you think the differences are in planes during Amelia Earhart's day and the jets that are used today.

Math Practice: Fractions

Subtract these fractions with like denominators. Then solve problem 5.

1. $\dfrac{7}{8} - \dfrac{2}{8} =$ _____	2. $\dfrac{12}{15} - \dfrac{3}{15} =$ _____	3. $8\dfrac{3}{4} - \dfrac{1}{4} =$ _____

4.	5. Javier wants to buy CDs with his birthday money. He received $30.00 from his grandma. If each CD cost $14.97, how many CD's can he buy?
$5\dfrac{9}{12} - 4\dfrac{1}{12} =$ _____	_____

Language Practice: Analogies

Complete each analogy.

1. Orange is to fruit as almond is to _____.

2. Foot is to shoe and _____ is to glove.

3. Remote is to _____ as joystick is to video game.

4. Snow is to shovel as _____ is to back-hoe.

5. _____ is to hot as black is to white.

6. Stripes are to tigers as spots are to _____.

 Writing Practice: Write a paragraph using the title below.

Things I Remember Most About Kindergarten

Math Practice: Variables

Fill in the blanks. Then solve problem 5.

1. If $6 + a = 10$, then $a =$ _____	2. If $20 - b = 15$, then $b =$ _____	3. If $4 \times c = 40$, then $c =$ _____

4. If $50 \div d = 25$, then $d =$ _____	5. Your neighbor Mr. Jones is paying you to walk his dog Tubbs. If he gives you $0.50 a day, how many days will it take to earn $10.00? _____

Language Practice: Verbs

Complete each sentence by adding a compound verb.

1. The rabbits _____ and _____ in the forest.

2. The squirrels _____ and _____ up the tree.

3. The snake _____ and _____ along the ground.

4. The lions _____ and _____ in their cages.

5. The baby birds _____ and _____ in their nests.

 Writing Practice: Do you have a favorite poster on the wall in your room at home? Do you collect things? Write a descriptive paragraph describing your room.

Math Practice: Decimals

For problems 1 and 2, write each decimal in numbers. For problems 3 and 4, write each decimal in words. Then solve problem 5.

1. ninety-eight and six tenths _____	2. two thousand forty and eighty-two hundredths _____	3. 114.7 _____ _____ _____
4. 26.54 _____ _____ _____		5. Juanita has to be at school at 8:00. If it takes her 15 minutes to get dressed, 12 minutes to eat breakfast, 5 minutes to brush her teeth, and 8 minutes to get to school, what time does she need to get up? _____

Language Practice: Alphabetical Order

Put the names of Santa's reindeer in alphabetical order.

Dasher   _____

Dancer   _____

Prancer   _____

Vixen   _____

Comet   _____

Cupid   _____

Donner   _____

Blitzen   _____

Rudolph   _____

✍ **Writing Practice:** Write your own holiday fantasy.

Math Practice: Fractions

Change to mixed numerals. Then solve problem 5.

1. $\frac{17}{4}$ = _____	2. $\frac{23}{5}$ = _____	3. $\frac{47}{7}$ = _____
4. $\frac{99}{10}$ = _____		5. Tom played football for his school team. He made three touchdowns. His friend made two touchdowns. How many points did they score in the game? (**Hint:** touchdown = 6 points) _____

Language Practice: Sentence/Fragment

Add the correct end mark to each complete sentence. Write a **F** if the sentence is incomplete.

1. Go fishing with Dad _____

2. The girls watching a scary movie _____

3. Hamilton read six books this month _____

4. He can teach his parrot to talk _____

5. A man in the boat _____

6. A million stars in the sky _____

7. We went to English class. We worked on our language sentences _____

8. Our teacher gave us treats for Valentine's Day _____

Writing Practice: Write your own fairy tale about a frog and a princess.

Math Practice: Geometry

Fill in the missing answer and draw a picture of the shape. Then solve problem 5.

1. A pentagon has _____ sides.	2. A hexagon has _____ sides.	3. An octagon has _____ sides.

4. Kelly, DeWayne, Jerika, and Edgar went to a masquerade party. They were dressed as a lion, tiger, bear, and cougar, but not in that order. Jerika was not the cougar, and Edgar's costume did not have a long tail. Kelly was either the tiger or the bear. What were each person's costume?

Kelly = _____

DeWayne = _____

Jerika = _____

Edgar = _____

Language Practice: Consonant Blends

Add two different blends *(scr, spl, shr, spr, str, thr)* to each word ending to make two new words.

1. _____eam   _____eam
2. _____ing   _____ing
3. _____ash   _____ash
4. _____ill   _____ill
5. _____ead   _____ead
6. _____ap   _____ap
7. _____ee   _____ee
8. _____ew   _____ew

 Writing Practice: There are only a few types of animals that live in the Arctic. Write about how you would like or dislike living in the Arctic.

Name _____

Math Practice: Sets

Look at the following set of whole numbers through ten {0, 1, 2, 3, 4, 5, 6, 7, 8, 9, 10}. Using this set, list the sets below. Then solve problem 5.

1. even numbers { _____ }	2. odd numbers { _____ }	3. numbers divisible by 5 { _____ }

4. numbers divisible by three { _____ }	5. Bobbie is going to a party. He has to leave by 5:00. Before he can go, he has to finish his chores (15 min.), walk his sister to her friend's house (5 min.), get air put in his bike tire (10 min.), and finish his homework (25 min.). If he gets home from school at 3:30, how much time is left to get dressed? _____

Language Practice: Fact or Opinion

Write **F** if the statement is fact and **O** if the statement is opinion.

_____ 1. Piglets are cute baby pigs.

_____ 2. People may live in space someday.

_____ 3. An oyster has a shell.

_____ 4. There are aliens on Mars.

_____ 5. Libraries are fun to visit.

_____ 6. Water is necessary for humans to live.

_____ 7. Strawberries are delicious.

_____ 8. It is fun to play in the snow.

Writing Practice: Write a story using the sentence starter below.

It was so unfair . . .

Math Practice: Variables

For problems 1–4, fill in the blanks. Then solve problem 5.

1. If 10 + *e* = 32, then *e* = _____	2. If 21 − *f* = 10, then *f* = _____	3. If 6 x *g* = 48, then *g* = _____
4. If 99 ÷ *h* = 11, then *h* = _____	5. The perimeter of a square is 20 inches. How long is each side? _____	

Language Practice: Commas

Write a sentence that corresponds with each comma rule. Be sure to use the comma correctly.

1. Use a comma to separate items in a list.

   _____

2. Use a comma to set off direct quotes.

   _____

3. Use a comma to separate the names of cities and states.

   _____

4. Use a comma to set off a direct address.

   _____

5. Use a comma and a connecting word to connect two clauses.

   _____

 Writing Practice: There are over 250,000 kinds of flowers. Flowers are given to people sometimes to help them feel better. Write a story about either getting flowers or giving flowers and how it made you feel.

Math Practice: Percents/Fractions

For problems 1–4, write each percent as a fraction. Make sure to reduce each answer. Then solve problem 5.

1. 17% = _____	2. 35% = _____	3. 75% = _____
4. 20% = _____	5. The perimeter of a triangle is 58 meters. One side is 18 meters long, and another side is 25 meters long. How long is the third side? _____	

Language Practice: Possessives

Write the correct possessive in the blank.

1. The cat has a toy mouse. Evan played with the _____ toy mouse.

2. My sisters have dolls. My _____ dolls are fun to play with.

3. Sue Ellen is on the basketball team. We saw _____ team play yesterday.

4. Her uncle has a bicycle shop. Her _____ bicycle shop is on Third Street.

5. The pencils belong to the students. The _____ pencils were on their desks.

6. The birds sing merrily. The _____ song is sweet to hear.

Writing Practice: Write a paragraph using the sentence starter below.

"Well, it's about time you came . . ."

Name _____

Math Practice: Decimals/Fractions

Write the following decimals as a fraction. Then solve problem 5.

1. 0.67 = _____	2. 0.9 = _____	3. 0.212 = _____

4. 0.49 = _____	5. A grasshopper can jump 3 feet high and 20 times its length. If a grasshopper is 3.5 inches long, how far can it jump? _____

Language Practice: Abbreviations

Unscramble the name of the state. Then match it to its abbreviation.

Nickname	State	Abbreviations	Abbreviations
1. Heart of Dixie	(AAAAMBL) _____	_____	IA
2. Last Frontier	(AAAKSL) _____	_____	ID
3. Grand Canyon State	(AANROZI) _____	_____	IN
4. Land of Opportunity	(AAASKRNS) _____	_____	IL
5. Gem State	(IOHAD) _____	_____	AZ
6. Land of Lincoln	(IIILSLNO) _____	_____	AR
7. Hoosier State	(IIAANND) _____	_____	AL
8. Hawkeye State	(IAOW) _____	_____	AK

 Writing Practice: Hawaii is the only state that is a group of islands. Write a story about being alone on an island.

Math Practice: Fractions

For problems 1–4, add the mixed numbers. Then solve problem 5.

1. $8\frac{2}{7} + 4\frac{3}{7} =$ _____	2. $5\frac{2}{5} + 6\frac{1}{5} =$ _____	3. $9\frac{3}{8} + 1\frac{4}{8} =$ _____

4.

$6\frac{2}{9} + 6\frac{5}{9} =$ _____

5. Jimmy lives $\frac{1}{3}$ of a mile away from the baseball field. If he walks there in the morning, back home for lunch, back to the field, and then back home for dinner, how far has he walked?

_____

Language Practice: Analogies

Complete each analogy.

1. dog is to puppy as cow is to _____

2. ship is to sail as car is to _____

3. book is to read as music is to _____

4. on is to off as here is to _____

5. come is to came as some is to _____

6. pencil is to paper as paintbrush is to _____

7. tan is to brown as pink is to _____

8. milk is to cup as coffee is to _____

 Writing Practice: Create a newspaper article with the heading below.

Extra! Extra! Read All About It!

Name _____

Math Practice: Fractions

For problems 1–4, subtract the mixed numbers. Then solve problem 5.

1. $12\frac{8}{9} - 7\frac{7}{9} =$ _____	2. $15\frac{5}{8} - 9\frac{2}{8} =$ _____	3. $22\frac{2}{3} - 11\frac{1}{3} =$ _____

4.

$16\frac{4}{5} - 8\frac{2}{5} =$ _____

5. The perimeter of an octagon is 40 feet. All the sides have equal length. How long are they?

_____

Language Practice: Capitalization

Write a sentence that corresponds with each capitalization rule. Be sure to use correct capital letters.

1. Begin every sentence with a capital letter.

_____

2. Proper nouns begin with capital letters (city, state, street, river, etc.).

_____

3. The pronoun I is always capitalized.

_____

4. Titles are capitalized when they are used before names.

_____

5. Capitalize the first and last word and all other important words in the titles of books.

_____

6. All holidays, days of the week, and months of the year begin with a capital letter.

_____

✎ **Writing Practice:** On a separate piece of paper, finish the story below.

Yesterday, I was walking down the street and a stranger stopped me. I was frightened, but he only wanted help.

Name _____

Math Practice: Measurement

For problems 1–4, fill in the blanks. Then solve problem 5.

1. $\frac{2}{3}$ yd. = _____ feet	2. $\frac{3}{4}$ hr. = _____ minutes	3. $\frac{1}{2}$ doz. = _____ eggs

4.

$\frac{1}{4}$ ft. = _____ inches

5. A jar of candy has 592 pieces in it. Each bag of candy used to fill up the jar contained 30 pieces.

How many bags were needed to fill the jar?

_____

How many extra pieces of candy were left over?

_____

Language Practice: Handwriting

Write this poem in your best handwriting.

Bugs

I like bugs.
Black bugs, green bugs,
Bad bugs, mean bugs,
Any kind of bug.
A bug in a rug, a bug in the grass,
A bug on the sidewalk, a bug in a glass,
I like bugs.
Big bugs, fat bugs,
Shiny bugs, round bugs,
Lady bugs, buggy bugs,
I like bugs.
—Unknown

_____ (title)

_____

_____

_____

_____

_____

_____

_____

_____

_____

_____

Writing Practice: Write your own poem about an animal or insect that you like.

Name

Math Practice: Mathematical Terms

For problems 1–4, fill in the blanks. Then solve problem 5.

1. The sum of 84, 39, and 21 equals _____.	2. The difference of 2,341 and 1,885 is _____.	3. The product of 64 and 73 is _____.
4. The quotient of 360 and 9 is _____.	5. Baseball cards are 15 cents each or $1.39 for a package of 10. How much would you save if you bought the package instead of 10 individual cards? _____	

Language Practice: Adjectives

Circle each adjective in the story.

The Storm

Wow! Did we ever have a bad storm! Yesterday, we had cool temperature, but soon a warm front moved in from the north. It started to rain. Huge raindrops fell, and soon the wet grass became like a soggy sponge. Loud thunder and bright lightening filled the dark sky. We were frightfully scared. We lined up in the long hallway waiting till the ferocious storm passed. After ten minutes, the storm was over.

 Writing Practice: Write your first name vertically. Then, for each letter of your name, write an adjective describing yourself.

Math Practice: Mixed Review

For problems 1–4, fill in the blanks. Then solve problem 5.

1. The average of 6, 18, and 12 is _____.	2. In October, there are four full weeks and _____ days.	3. The time between 10:25 A.M. and 11:10 A.M. is _____ minutes.
4. One-third of the number 12 is _____.	5. In the classroom, there are 24 students. $\frac{1}{3}$ are reading, $\frac{1}{2}$ are doing math, and the rest are working on spelling. How many are working on spelling? _____	

Language Practice: Rhyming Words

Fill in the blanks of this poem with a word that rhymes.

Groundhog Day

This furry friend might come out once a year
To keep his shadow if the day is _____.
And on this very special Groundhog Day
If his shadow is seen, winter will _____.
For six more long weeks we'll have to keep warm,
But if it's cloudy, his shadow's not there
There'll soon be warm weather and days will be _____.
So please, Mr. Sun, just this one day,
Find a big dark cloud—and stay _____!

—Unknown

 Writing Practice: Write a story about a surprising turn of events when the groundhog sees his shadow.

Math Practice: Reading a Chart

Look at the chart. Answer the questions using the information from the chart.

1. Who is older, Jesse Jackson or Muhammad Ali? _____	2. How many years younger is Ali than Rosa Parks? _____	3. How many years older is Rosa Parks than Bill Cosby? _____

4. Jesse Owens was famous for running in track and field events. He was born in 1913 and died in 1980. How old was he when he died? _____	**Black American**	**Born**
	Bill Cosby	1937
	Rosa Parks	1913
	Shirley Chisholm	1924
	Jesse Jackson	1941
	Muhammad Ali	1942

Language Practice: Cause and Effect

Underline the cause in each sentence.

1. When Sally listens in class, she makes better grades.

2. We'll go outside for P.E. because the weather is nice.

3. If Betsy cleans her room, she'll be able to go to the mall.

4. April talked on the phone and ordered a pizza.

5. Jeff tried out for the lead in *Romeo and Juliet* and was chosen to play the part of Romeo.

6. We went to the ballgame, when my uncle came for a visit.

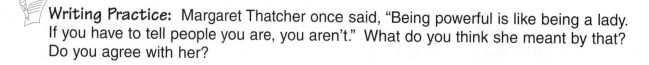 **Writing Practice:** Margaret Thatcher once said, "Being powerful is like being a lady. If you have to tell people you are, you aren't." What do you think she meant by that? Do you agree with her?

Math Practice: Fractions

For problems 1–4, fill in the blanks. Then solve problem 5.

1. $\frac{1}{8}$ of 16 = _____	2. $\frac{1}{3}$ of 24 = _____	3. $\frac{3}{4}$ of 12 = _____

4.

$\frac{1}{7}$ of 21 = _____

5. It is 398 miles to Aunt Edna's house. The train goes 80 miles per hour. About how many hours will it take to get to her house?

_____

Language Practice: Sequencing

Read the story. Number the sentences so that they are in correct order.

The Camping Trip

Dad told Ben that their scout camping trip would be on Friday. He told him to pack his bags. Ben thought about what he should pack. Then he packed his clothes, his camping gear, his scout manual, his football, and his sleeping bag. After he finished packing, he told his dad he was ready to go! Finally, on Friday, they left for the scout camping trip.

____ Ben and his dad went camping.

____ Dad told Ben about the camping trip.

____ Dad told Ben to pack.

____ Ben packed his clothes.

____ Ben decided what to pack.

 Writing Practice: You are going to make a time capsule about yourself. What would you put in your time capsule, and why?

Name _____

Math Practice: Mixed Review

For problems 1–4, fill in the blanks. Then solve problem 5.

1. One-fourth of 28 is _____.	2. Three weeks and 4 days would be _____ days in all.	3. Four cartons of eggs (Each carton equals a dozen.) is _____ eggs in all.
4. There are _____ degrees in a right angle.	5. Our club collected money to buy a gift for a sick classmate. In all, we collected 82 quarters, 90 dimes, 45 nickels, and 79 pennies. How much money was collected in all?	

Language Practice: Homonyms

Write *your* or *you're* in the blanks. Capitalize when necessary.

1. _____ cake was delicious.

2. _____ my closest friend.

3. I need _____ advice.

4. What is _____ name?

5. _____ from Minnesota.

6. _____ invited to my party.

7. _____ late for school.

8. _____ cat licked my hand.

 Writing Practice: Write a persuasive paragraph telling why you agree or disagree with having no smoking in public places.

Math Practice: Percentages/Fractions

For problems 1–4, write the fraction as a percentage. Then solve problem 5.

1. $\frac{1}{2} =$ _____ %	2. $\frac{1}{4} =$ _____ %	3. $\frac{1}{5} =$ _____ %

4. $\frac{1}{10} =$ _____ %

5. In a football game, a touchdown plus the extra point gets 7 points and a field goal gets 3 points. If one team's score is 15 points, how many touchdowns and field goals have they scored?

_____

Language Practice: Synonyms

Write a synonym for each underlined word.

1. You are <u>correct</u>. _____

2. It <u>arrived</u> yesterday. _____

3. Mom sang her baby a <u>lullaby</u>. _____

4. Ghosts don't <u>scare</u> me. _____

5. The students were <u>quiet</u>. _____

6. What was the <u>name</u> of the song? _____

7. The <u>shears</u> were sharp. _____

8. I sat on the <u>sofa</u>. _____

Writing Practice: Write a paragraph using the sentence starter below.

The last thing I want to do this year is . . .

Math Practice: Multiplication

For problems 1–4, find the GCF (greatest common factor) of the numbers listed below. Then solve problem 5.

1. 12, 15	2. 6, 9	3. 5, 15
_____	_____	_____

4. 18, 24	5. During the school's reading contest, a group of four students read a total of 50 books. Carol read twice as many books as Joe. Amy read 12 books. Joe read two less books than Amy, but two more books than Ling. How many books did they each read?
_____	Carol = _____ Amy = _____ Joe = _____ Ling = _____

Language Practice: Verb Usage

Write *sit* or *set* in each blank.

1. We don't _____ on the table.

2. Please _____ the book on your desk.

3. Al, _____ your lunch in your locker.

4. Lou, _____ here.

5. Did he _____ on my glove?

6. Where did Mrs. Johnson _____ the box of books?

Writing Practice: Write a paragraph using the sentence starter below.

We all make mistakes, and mine was . . .

Name _____

Math Practice: Multiplication

For problems 1–4, find the LCM (lowest common multiple) of the numbers listed below. Then solve problem 5.

1. 2, 3	2. 8, 12	3. 5, 15
_____	_____	_____

4. 4, 9	5. Marty lives 18 miles from her school. By rounding to the nearest ten, about how many miles is that?
_____	_____

Language Practice: Prefix/Suffix

Underline the base words.

1. disobey

2. teacher

3. unlike

4. tricycle

5. sickness

6. lovely

7. beginning

8. discover

9. misfortune

10. helpful

11. mindful

12. jumping

13. misplace

14. disassemble

15. reporting

 Writing Practice: Write a paragraph using the sentence starter below.

I looked everywhere, but I couldn't find my . . .

Math Practice: Equivalent Numbers

For problems 1–4, write <, >, or = in each blank. Then solve problem 5.

| 1. $\frac{1}{2}$ ◯ $\frac{3}{4}$ | 2. $\frac{2}{3}$ ◯ $\frac{4}{6}$ | 3. $\frac{1}{4}$ ◯ $\frac{1}{3}$ |

| 4. $\frac{2}{3}$ ◯ $\frac{4}{5}$ | 5. How much did a team pay for jerseys if each jersey cost $9.00 and the team bought 3 dozen? _____ |

Language Practice: Adjectives

Write the article *a* or *an* before each noun.

1. _____ house

2. _____ hour

3. _____ orange

4. _____ aunt

5. _____ job

6. _____ eye

7. _____ gorilla

8. _____ arm

9. _____ man

10. _____ old man

11. _____ elephant

12. _____ candy

13. _____ apple

14. _____ table

15. _____ chair

 Writing Practice: Write a story using the title below.

My Saddest Day

Name _____

Math Practice: Fractions

For problems 1–4, reduce the following fractions. Then solve problem 5.

1. $\frac{4}{6} =$ _____	2. $\frac{9}{18} =$ _____	3. $\frac{3}{15} =$ _____

4. $\frac{6}{8} =$ _____

5. The average speed limit on most highways is 65 miles per hour. If a car went exactly 65 mph, how far would it go in 5 hours?

_____

Language Practice: Story Comprehension

Read the story and answer the following questions.

The Kiwi

The kiwi is the national emblem of Australia. The kiwi is a bird, like the eagle of the U.S., yet the kiwi cannot fly. Years ago, the kiwi was hunted for its valuable feathers, just as the American eagle was. The kiwi is a nocturnal animal, which means it comes out at night and sleeps during the day. It is considered the strangest bird of all birds.

1. What makes the kiwi a different kind of bird? _____

2. How is the kiwi like the eagle? _____

3. What is a nocturnal animal? _____

4. Why do you think the kiwi is a strange bird? _____

Writing Practice: The turkey was almost named our national bird. Do you think the eagle was a better choice? Why or why not?

Name _____

Math Practice: Rounding

For problems 1–4, round each number to the nearest ten. Then solve problem 5.

1.	2.	3.
123 = _____	565 = _____	791 = _____

4.	5.
637 = _____	A long distance phone call costs $0.25 the first 3 minutes and $0.40 for any additional minutes. How much would it cost for a 10-minute phone call? _____

Language Practice: Plurals

Circle the correct plural.

1. **bridge**   a. bridges   b. bridgies

2. **boss**   a. boss's   b. bosses

3. **speech**   a. speechs   b. speeches

4. **chicken**   a. chickens   b. chickenes

5. **box**   a. boxs   b. boxes

6. **kiss**   a. kiss's   b. kisses

7. **bush**   a. bushses   b. bushes

8. **tomato**   a. tomatos   b. tomatoes

 Writing Practice: An igloo is a house made of blocks of snow. Write what you would like your house to be made of and why.

Math Practice: Mixed Computation

Solve each problem.

1. 468 + 129	2. 700 − 124	3. 325 x 32
4. 5)‾365	5. The library has about 140 mystery books, rounded to the nearest ten. What is the least number of mystery books in the library? _____

Language Practice: Capitalization

Circle all letters that should be capitalized in the following titles. Then rewrite them correctly.

1. "the big snow"

   _____

2. "clifford gets a job"

   _____

3. "all in the morning"

   _____

4. "i can read about birds"

   _____

5. "the prince and the pauper"

   _____

6. "georgie to the rescue"

   _____

7. "the story about ping"

   _____

8. "a weed is a flower"

   _____

Writing Practice: Write a paragraph using the sentence starter below.

I really get angry when . . .

Math Practice: Reading a Graph

Use the bar graph to answer each question.

1. Which city is the largest in population? _____	2. Which city has less than 100,000 in population? _____	3. Where does Nashville rank (first, second, third, fourth, fifth)? _____

4. Which two cities have almost the same amount in population?

_____

_____

5 Largest Cities in Tennessee

700
600
500
400
300
200
100
0

Memphis   Nashville   Knoxville   Chattanooga   Clarksville
*population in thousands

Language Practice: Direct Objects

Complete each sentence with a direct object.

1. Jamal closed the _____.

2. We ate our _____.

3. He caught the _____.

4. Mr. Blair wrote a _____.

5. Someone took my _____.

6. I like to ride my _____.

7. She read a _____.

8. I like to play _____.

Writing Practice: Write a paragraph using the sentence starter.

I remember when . . .

Math Practice: Division with Money

Solve each problem. Round to the nearest penny.

1. $2\overline{)\$11.97}$	2. $4\overline{)\$34.63}$	3. $3\overline{)\$49.06}$

4. $4\overline{)\$87.61}$	5. Sandra was given $12.00 for lunch at school for 5 days. How much can Sandra spend each day? _____

Language Practice: Homonyms

Write a sentence using each homonym.

1. hear _____

   here _____

2. sail _____

   sale _____

3. do _____

   dew _____

4. ate _____

   eight _____

✍ **Writing Practice:** Write a paragraph using the sentence starter below.

I couldn't believe I got caught . . .

Math Practice: Multiplication

Solve each problem.

1. 2 x 3 x 4 = _____	2. 7 x 5 x 6 = _____	3. 9 x 2 x 9 = _____
4. 4 x 3 x 12 = _____	5. There are 60 minutes in an hour. How many minutes are in 24 hours? _____	

Language Practice: Negatives

Write **C** for correctly used negatives and **I** for incorrectly used negatives.

_____ 1. I don't have no homework.

_____ 2. Christopher doesn't have nothing to do.

_____ 3. She hasn't got a pencil.

_____ 4. Fishing is no good with this boat.

_____ 5. Dad didn't catch no fish today.

_____ 6. I think this food is no good.

_____ 7. We didn't bring any treats to the party.

_____ 8. We don't want nothing to eat.

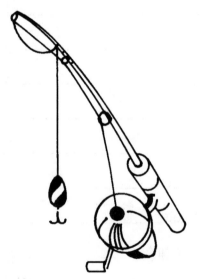

 Writing Practice: Write a story using the title, "My Life."

Math Practice: Multiplication with Money

Solve each problem.

1. $45.21 x 21	2. $3.82 x 14	3. $5.25 x 30
4. $92.98 x 8	5. During Columbus' last voyage, only 116 men survived. One hundred forty men began the voyage. How many did not survive? _____	

Language Practice: Contractions

Rewrite the underlined words with a contraction.

_____ 1. <u>There is</u> time to read before going to bed.

_____ 2. <u>That is</u> the first one I have read in a while.

_____ 3. <u>I would</u> like to read a mystery novel.

_____ 4. I <u>cannot</u> read for very long.

_____ 5. The book <u>should not</u> take but a few days to read.

_____ 6. It <u>does not</u> look too hard.

_____ 7. <u>I will</u> get a new book when I finish.

Writing Practice: Write a paragraph using the sentence starter below.

My goals for the new year are . . .

Math Practice: Mean

For problems 1–4, find the averages of these test scores. Then solve problem 5.

1. Billy: 85, 88, 95 _____	2. Jorge: 99, 100, 81 _____	3. Joanne: 89, 89, 93 _____

4. Jaquarius: 90, 80, 88 _____	5. Simon and his friend Wayne set up a lemonade stand. A cup of lemonade cost $0.25 each. They made $5.00. How many cups of lemonade did they sell? _____

Language Practice: Compound Words

Make a compound word by adding a beginning or an ending to the words below.

1. _____ground

2. grand_____

3. book_____

4. _____plane

5. him_____

6. _____age

7. every_____

8. with_____

9. sun_____

10. _____ball

11. _____man

12. home_____

 Writing Practice: Imagine waking up and finding out you're 10 feet tall. Write a story about your adventures.

Math Practice: Estimation

For problems 1–4, choose which answer is closest to what you have estimated. Then solve problem 5.

1. How many bites does it take to eat a banana?	2. How much does your book bag weigh?	3. How many students are in your grade?
a. 10 b. 20 c. 30	a. 10 lbs. b. 20 lbs. c. 30 lbs.	a. 50 b. 100 c. 150

4. How tall is your math teacher?	5. Cleo bought lunch at the mall. She had $13.00 in her purse. If a sandwich cost $4.00, a soda cost $1.50, and a piece of cake cost $2.00, how much change will she receive?
a. 5 ft. b. 6 ft. c. 7 ft.	_____

Language Practice: Prepositions

Circle the prepositions in each sentence.

1. The blanket is laying over the chair.

2. The pencil is under the oak stool.

3. Please get me the cleaner above the shelf.

4. Maggie is sitting beside David.

5. Place the napkins on the table.

6. The dog went under the ball.

7. We live by the noisiest street.

8. The glass cleaner is below the laundry soap.

 Writing Practice: Sometimes pets act like members of the family. Do you have a pet like that? If you do, write about how your pet acts. If you don't have a pet, write a story about a pet.

Math Practice: Fractions/Decimals/Percents

For problems 1–4, fill in the blanks on the chart. Then solve problem 5.

1. Fraction = $\frac{33}{100}$ Decimal = _____ Percent = 33%	2. Fraction = _____ Decimal = .54 Percent = 54%	3. Fraction = $\frac{77}{100}$ Decimal = .77 Percent = _____
4. Fraction = $\frac{12}{100}$ Decimal = _____ Percent = 12%	5. A television Joe wanted cost $185.00. He noticed the store put it on sale at 25% off. How much would the television cost after the discount? _____	

Language Practice: Compound Sentences

Add a connecting word and finish each sentence to make a compound sentence.

1. My best friend is nice, _____

   _____.

2. Our cat likes to lay on the couch, _____

   _____.

3. My math teacher is strict, _____

   _____.

4. Mac sings in the shower, _____

   _____.

5. Harry wants to go bowling, _____

   _____.

 **Writing Practice:** Write a story using the sentence starter below.

I went ice skating on the pond, when suddenly I heard a cracking sound . . .

Math Practice: Mathematical Terms

For problems 1–4, circle the letter of its meaning. Then solve problem 5.

1. deci- a. hundredth b. millionth c. tenth d. thousandth	2. centi- a. hundredth b. millionth c. tenth d. thousandth	3. milli- a. hundredth b. millionth c. tenth d. thousandth
4. micro- a. hundredth b. millionth c. tenth d. thousandth	5. The baseball team sold 45 cans of soda, 24 bars of candy, and 10 bags of popcorn. They all cost $0.50. How much money did the team make? _____	

Language Practice: Abbreviation/Punctuation

Circle the abbreviations that need periods.

Mr	pm	CIA	COD	CD
MD	BC	TN	oz	FL
TV	qt	St	RSVP	Rd
km	Dr	USA	US	in

 Writing Practice: Alexander had a no good, very bad day. Write about your no good, very bad day.

Math Practice: Addition with Money

Solve each problem.

1. $654.88 + $98.92 = _____	2. $9,832.11 + $903.45 = _____	3. $54.00 + $87.38 = _____
4. $99.99 + $11.11 = _____	5. Amanda bought 5 shirts in the mall for $9.99 each. How much did she spend in all? _____	

Language Practice: Parts of Speech

Match each part of speech with its definition.

_____ 1. noun   a. describe noun or pronoun

_____ 2. pronoun   b. names a person, place, thing, or idea

_____ 3. verb   c. connects words

_____ 4. adjective   d. express action or state of being

_____ 5. adverb   e. takes the place of a noun

_____ 6. preposition   f. shows emotion or surprise

_____ 7. interjection   g. describes a verb

_____ 8. conjunction   h. relates a noun to another word

 Writing Practice: You're walking on the beach and you look down and see a bottle. It has a message inside. Write about what it says.

Name _____

Math Practice: Subtraction with Money

Solve each problem.

1. $654.88 − $98.92 =	2. $9,832.11 − $903.45 =	3. $54.00 − $37.38 =

4. $99.99 − $11.11 =

5. A 12-pack of soft drinks sells for $3.99. If bought separately, the cans would cost $0.60 each. How much do you save by buying the 12-pack?

Language Practice: Context Clues

Circle which meaning best describes the underlined word.

1. The grackle flew through the air.
   a. shark   b. bird   c. insect
2. The skull went so fast, it almost tipped over into the water.
   a. boat   b. car   c. ski
3. Treating the animal with kindness was humane.
   a. horrible   b. not acceptable   c. merciful
4. The fallow seeds were still laying on the ground.
   a. unplanted   b. planted   c. rooted
5. If you don't brush your teeth, they may have caries.
   a. decay   b. enamel   c. caps
6. The lapidary was careful to not break the gems.
   a. someone who protects animals   b. someone who protects stones
   c. someone who protects people

Writing Practice: Can you imagine yourself as a parent? What would you do if you were a parent? How would you raise your children?

Math Practice: Place Value

Answer the questions.

1. Write 3,456,100 in expanded form. _____ _____ _____	2. Write 672,008 in expanded form. _____ _____ _____	3. Write 20,000 + 8,000 + 300 + 9 in standard form. _____
4. Write 4,000,000 + 100,000 + 20,000 + 9,000 + 80 + 1 in standard form. _____	5. Teresa bought a cheeseburger for $1.50, French fries for $0.50, and a soda for $0.75. How much did she pay for her meal? _____	

Language Practice: Comprehension

Answer questions about the following facts.

Facts About Fish

- All fish live in water.
- Most fish have scales.
- Some are catfish.
- Some fish live in fresh water.
- All fish are cold-blooded.
- Some fish live in salt water.

1. Is it true that all fish live in fresh water? _____

2. Is it true that all fish have scales? _____

3. Is it true that all catfish live in water? _____

4. Is it true that catfish are cold-blooded? _____

Writing Practice: Write a paragraph using the sentence starter below.

Being a part of a family means . . .

Math Practice: Number Sentences

Write a number sentence for each word problem and solve.

1. Clarence had 139 baseball cards. He gave 23 to Allen. How many cards does he have left? _____	2. At the dollar store, I spent $6.48. I gave the cashier a 10 dollar bill. How much money should I get back? _____	3. I bought a pencil for $0.25, an eraser for $0.05, and a pack of paper for $0.75. How much did I spend in all? _____
4. Josiah had a pack of notebook paper with 150 sheets. He gave four friends 6 pieces of paper each. How many sheets does he have left? _____	5. Ramon wants to take his 375 gumballs and put them in machines. Each machine can only hold 10 gumballs. What is the greatest number of gumball machines Ramon needs? _____	

Language Practice: Figurative Language

Finish each hyperbole.

1. It rained so hard _____

2. It was so hot _____

3. My cat is so lazy _____

4. It was so foggy _____

5. My little sister is so annoying _____

6. The room was so crowded _____

Writing Practice: Write a paragraph using the sentence starter below.

If there's one thing I really dislike, it's . . .

Name _____

Math Practice: Addition

Add the numbers in each column. Then solve problem 5.

1.	98	2.	145	3.	2,965
	76		163		4,526
	54		237		2,632
	+ 32		+ 846		+ 5,038

4.   10,132
         12,573
         35,742
       + 54,624

5. Doreen went shopping and spent all of her money. Her total purchases were $87.35. How much change did she receive? What else do you need to know about this problem?
   a. what she bought
   b. how much money she gave the cashier
   c. you have all you need to know

Language Practice: Adverbs

Write a word before each **-ly** to make a sentence using adverbs.

1. _____ly he sang to the baby.

2. I listened _____ly to the teacher.

3. She worked _____ly on her assignment.

4. They _____ly joined in the search for the missing wallet.

5. The band played _____ly.

6. That is a _____ly nice picture you painted.

Writing Practice: When you are feeling unhappy, what do you do? Write about how you begin to feel happy again.

#3302 Daily Skills Practice—Grades 4–5   198   ©Teacher Created Materials, Inc.

Name _____

Math Practice: Number Order

Solve the problems.

1. Write in order from least to greatest. 98,765 _____ 987.65 _____ 9,876.5 _____ 98.765 _____	2. Write in order from least to greatest. 104.235 _____ 10,423.5 _____ 1,042.35 _____ 10.4235 _____	3. Write in order from greatest to least. 989 _____ 898 _____ 999 _____ 899 _____
4. Write in order from greatest to least. 2,003,005 _____ 200,300.5 _____ 20,030.05 _____ 2,003.005 _____	5. Noah brought 2 of most every kind of animal into the ark. If there were 189 kinds of animals, how many animals were in the ark? _____	

Language Practice: Interjections

Write an interjection before each sentence.

1. _____! Watch out for that car!

2. _____! That hurt!

3. _____! We won the game!

4. _____! I hate squash!

5. _____! The football team lost!

6. _____! I won the contest!

 Writing Practice: Write a story using the starter below.

We heard a noise and ran to the bush. There we saw . . .

Name _____

Math Practice: Division

Solve each problem.

1. $8\overline{)8,923}$	2. $5\overline{)45.95}$	3. $12\overline{)24,840}$
4. $11\overline{)776,655}$	5. Shawn read 78 pages in the novel *The Giver*. If there are 321 pages, how many more pages does he have to read? _____	

Language Practice: Vocabulary

Match the word with the definition.

_____ 1. moving air   a. air

_____ 2. water falling to the earth in drops   b. wind

_____ 3. study of weather   c. rain

_____ 4. cloud close to the ground   d. sleet

_____ 5. frozen rain   e. barometer

_____ 6. sound that follows lightning   f. fog

_____ 7. instrument used to measure air pressure   g. meteorology

_____ 8. invisible mixture of gases surrounding the earth   h. thunder

 Writing Practice: Have you ever wanted to be a famous athlete? What sport would you be famous for? Write about how you would become famous.

Math Practice: Multiplication/Decimals

Solve each problem.

1. 0.06 x 0.6 = _____	2. 0.4 x 30.2 = _____	3. 5 x 0.05 = _____
4. 6.0 x 0.7 = _____	5. 25 students were asked how often they read a book. 10 said they read at least 5 days a week. What percentage of the students read at least 5 days a week? _____	

Language Practice: Analogies

Complete each analogy.

1. Wings are to butterflies, as fins are to _____.

2. Chimney is to house, as _____ is to mountain.

3. Mother is to child, as cow is to _____.

4. Pen is to chicken, as _____ is to horse.

5. 5 is to pentagon, as 8 is to _____.

6. Grapes are to jelly, as apples are to _____.

7. Antlers are to deer, as _____ are to unicorns.

8. Pencils are to writing instruments, as _____ are to tools.

 Writing Practice: Picture yourself 10 years from now. What do you think you'll be doing? Write about it.

Math Practice: Mixed Review

Solve each problem.

1. $(40 + 3) - (20 + 12) =$ _____	2. $(60 + 8) - (34 + 8) =$ _____	3. $(6 \times 9) - (9 \times 4) =$ _____
4. $(8 \times 8) - (7 \times 7) =$ _____	5. 28 fifth graders were asked about their favorite ice cream. 14 said chocolate, and the others said vanilla. What percentage likes chocolate? _____	

Language Practice: Prefix

Answer each question about prefixes.

1. If **mis** means *wrong*, what does:

   a. mistreat mean?_____

   b. misread mean?_____

2. If **re** means *do again*, what does:

   a. repaint mean? _____

   b. retell mean? _____

3. If **un** means *not*, what does:

   a. untied mean? _____

   b. uncover mean?_____

 Writing Practice: Write a story with the title below.

The Case of the Missing Clock

Math Practice: Patterns

For problems 1–4, fill in the missing blanks. Then solve problem 5.

1. 10, _____, _____, _____, _____, 60	**2.** 3, _____, _____, 15, _____, _____	**3.** 12, _____, _____, _____, _____, 72

4. _____, 5, _____, 13, _____, 21, _____	**5.** Tom needs 40 liters of gas to fill his camper. How much will it cost if gas sells for $1.12 a liter? _____

Language Practice: Suffix

Answer each question about suffixes.

1. If **ful** means *full of*, what does:

   a. beautiful mean? _____

   b. joyful mean? _____

2. If **less** means *without*, what does:

   a. senseless mean? _____

   b. hopeless mean? _____

3. If **er** means *one who*, what does:

   a. teacher mean? _____

   b. painter mean? _____

Writing Practice: Write a story using the sentence starter below.

Slowly the door opened with a creaking sound . . .

Math Practice: Measurement

For problems 1–4, write the correct answers. Then solve problem 5.

1. At 100° C, do you take a bath or boil eggs? _____	2. At 0° C, do you freeze ice cream or cook hotdogs? _____	3. At 35° C, do you wear a bathing suit or wear a jacket? _____
4. At 40° C, are you at the North Pole or the Sahara Desert? _____	5. If John was cold, and he looked at the thermometer and it said 32°, would it be Celsius or Fahrenheit? _____	

Language Practice: Adverb/Verb

Underline the verb and circle each adverb.

1. The football player fell down.

2. The old dog just lies there.

3. The fire trucks drove nearby.

4. The pool table sits downstairs in the den.

5. The young baby crawled over to me.

6. The big dogs barked loudly.

7. The jet plane landed today.

8. My good friend arrives tomorrow.

 Writing Practice: Write a story using the sentence starter below.

In the year 2020 . . .

Math Practice: Variables

For problems 1–4, find the variable. Then solve problem 5.

1. $56 + 6 = x + 13$ $x =$ _____	2. $25 + 7 = 20 + y$ $y =$ _____	3. $66 - 6 = 72 - x$ $x =$ _____

4. $87 - 8 = y - 9$ $y =$ _____	5. Samuel paid for a new jacket. The jacket cost $24.98. His change was $15.02. How much money did he give the clerk? _____

Language Practice: Synonyms

Write a synonym for each word.

1. scarce _____

2. alarm _____

3. joyful _____

4. startle _____

5. identical _____

6. jersey _____

7. mammoth _____

8. valuable _____

 Writing Practice: Write a story using the sentence starter.

I was home by myself when I heard a noise in the attic . . .

Math Practice:

Language Practice:

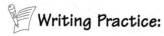 **Writing Practice:**

Page 4

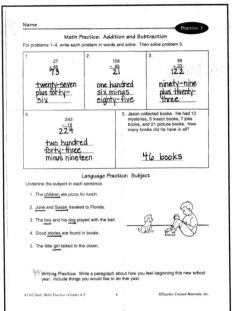

Name

Practice 1

Math Practice: Addition and Subtraction

For problems 1–4, write each problem in words and solve. Then solve problem 5.

| 1. 27 +46 **73** twenty-seven plus forty-six | 2. 106 – 85 **21** one hundred six minus eighty-five | 3. 99 +23 **122** ninety-nine plus twenty-three |
| 4. 243 – 19 **224** two hundred forty-three minus nineteen | 5. Jason collected books. He had 13 mysteries, 5 insect books, 7 joke books, and 21 picture books. How many books did he have in all? **46 books** | |

Language Practice: Subject

Underline the subject in each sentence.

1. The children ate pizza for lunch.
2. June and Susan traveled to Florida.
3. The boy and his dog played with the ball.
4. Good stories are found in books.
5. The little girl talked to the clown.

Writing Practice: Write a paragraph about how you feel beginning this new school year. Include things you would like to do this year.

#3302 Daily Skills Practice—Grades 4–5   4   ©Teacher Created Materials, Inc.

Page 5

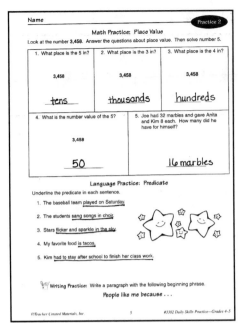

Name

Practice 2

Math Practice: Place Value

Look at the number 3,458. Answer the questions about place value. Then solve number 5.

| 1. What place is the 5 in? 3,458 **tens** | 2. What place is the 3 in? 3,458 **thousands** | 3. What place is the 4 in? 3,458 **hundreds** |
| 4. What is the number value of the 5? 3,458 **50** | 5. Joe had 32 marbles and gave Anita and Kim 8 each. How many did he have for himself? **16 marbles** | |

Language Practice: Predicate

Underline the predicate in each sentence.

1. The baseball team played on Saturday.
2. The students sang songs in choir.
3. Stars flicker and sparkle in the sky.
4. My favorite food is tacos.
5. Kim had to stay after school to finish her class work.

Writing Practice: Write a paragraph with the following beginning phrase.

People like me because . . .

©Teacher Created Materials, Inc.   5   #3302 Daily Skills Practice—Grades 4–5

Page 6

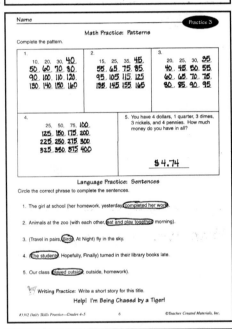

Name

Practice 3

Math Practice: Patterns

Complete the pattern.

| 1. 10, 20, 30, **40** **50, 60, 70, 80** **90, 100, 110, 120,** **130, 140, 150, 160** | 2. 15, 25, 35, **45** **55, 65, 75, 85,** **95, 105, 115, 125** **135, 145, 155, 165** | 3. 20, 25, 30, **35** **40, 45, 50, 55** **60, 65, 70, 75** **80, 85, 90, 95** |
| 4. 25, 50, 75, **100** **125, 150, 175, 200,** **225, 250, 275, 300,** **325, 350, 375, 400** | 5. You have 4 dollars, 1 quarter, 3 dimes, 3 nickels, and 4 pennies. How much money do you have in all? **$4.74** | |

Language Practice: Sentences

Circle the correct phrase to complete the sentences.

1. The girl at school (her homework, yesterday, completed her work).
2. Animals at the zoo (with each other, eat and play together, morning).
3. (Travel in pairs, Birds, At Night) fly in the sky.
4. (The students, Hopefully, Finally) turned in their library books late.
5. Our class (played outside, outside, homework).

Writing Practice: Write a short story for this title.

Help! I'm Being Chased by a Tiger!

#3302 Daily Skills Practice—Grades 4–5   6   ©Teacher Created Materials, Inc.

Page 7

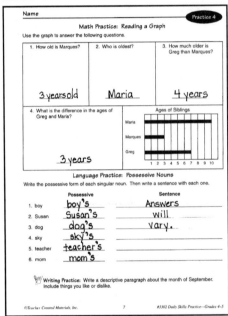

Name

Practice 4

Math Practice: Reading a Graph

Use the graph to answer the following questions.

| 1. How old is Marques? **3 years old** | 2. Who is oldest? **Maria** | 3. How much older is Greg than Marques? **4 years** |
| 4. What is the difference in the ages of Greg and Maria? **3 years** | Ages of Siblings (Maria, Marques, Greg graph) | |

Language Practice: Possessive Nouns

Write the possessive form of each singular noun. Then write a sentence with each one.

	Possessive	Sentence
1. boy	**boy's**	Answers
2. Susan	**Susan's**	will
3. dog	**dog's**	vary.
4. sky	**sky's**	
5. teacher	**teacher's**	
6. mom	**mom's**	

Writing Practice: Write a descriptive paragraph about the month of September. Include things you like or dislike.

©Teacher Created Materials, Inc.   7   #3302 Daily Skills Practice—Grades 4–5

Page 8

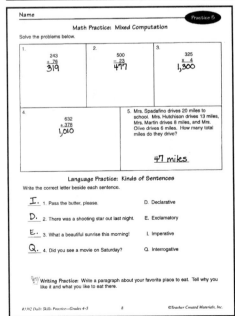

Name

Practice 5

Math Practice: Mixed Computation

Solve the problems below.

| 1. 243 + 76 **319** | 2. 500 – 23 **477** | 3. 325 x 4 **1,300** |
| 4. 632 + 378 **1,010** | 5. Mrs. Spadafino drives 20 miles to school. Mrs. Hutchison drives 13 miles, Mrs. Martin 8 miles, and Mrs. Olive drives 6 miles. How many total miles do they drive? **47 miles** | |

Language Practice: Kinds of Sentences

Write the correct letter beside each sentence.

I. 1. Pass the butter, please.   D. Declarative
D. 2. There was a shooting star out last night.   E. Exclamatory
E. 3. What a beautiful sunrise this morning!   I. Imperative
Q. 4. Did you see a movie on Saturday?   Q. Interrogative

Writing Practice: Write a paragraph about your favorite place to eat. Tell why you like it and what you like to eat there.

#3302 Daily Skills Practice—Grades 4–5   8   ©Teacher Created Materials, Inc.

Page 9

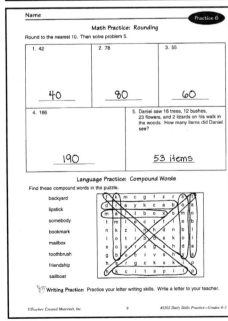

Name

Practice 6

Math Practice: Rounding

Round to the nearest 10. Then solve problem 5.

| 1. 42 **40** | 2. 78 **80** | 3. 55 **60** |
| 4. 186 **190** | 5. Daniel saw 16 trees, 12 bushes, 23 flowers, and 2 lizards on his walk in the woods. How many items did Daniel see? **53 items** | |

Language Practice: Compound Words

Find these compound words in the puzzle.

backyard
lipstick
somebody
bookmark
mailbox
toothbrush
friendship
sailboat

Writing Practice: Practice your letter writing skills. Write a letter to your teacher.

©Teacher Created Materials, Inc.   9   #3302 Daily Skills Practice—Grades 4–5

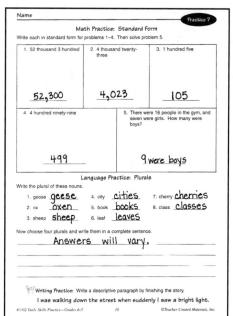

Name

Math Practice: Standard Form — Practice 7

Write each in standard form for problems 1–4. Then solve problem 5.

1. 52 thousand 3 hundred	2. 4 thousand twenty-three	3. 1 hundred five
52,300	4,023	105

4. 4 hundred ninety-nine	5. There were 16 people in the gym, and seven were girls. How many were boys?
499	9 were boys

Language Practice: Plurals

Write the plural of these nouns.

1. goose **geese**   4. city **cities**   7. cherry **cherries**
2. ox **oxen**   5. book **books**   8. class **classes**
3. sheep **sheep**   6. leaf **leaves**

Now choose four plurals and write them in a complete sentence.

Answers will vary.

Writing Practice: Write a descriptive paragraph by finishing the story.
I was walking down the street when suddenly I saw a bright light.

#3302 Daily Skills Practice—Grades 4–5   10   ©Teacher Created Materials, Inc.

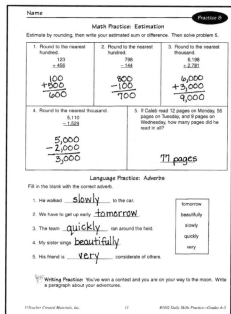

Name

Math Practice: Estimation — Practice 8

Estimate by rounding, then write your estimated sum or difference. Then solve problem 5.

1. Round to the nearest hundred.	2. Round to the nearest hundred.	3. Round to the nearest thousand.
123 + 456	798 − 144	6,198 + 2,781
100 + 500 = 600	800 − 100 = 700	6,000 + 3,000 = 9,000

4. Round to the nearest thousand.	5. If Caleb read 12 pages on Monday, 56 pages on Tuesday, and 9 pages on Wednesday, how many pages did he read in all?
5,110 − 1,529 = 5,000 − 2,000 = 3,000	77 pages

Language Practice: Adverbs

Fill in the blank with the correct adverb.

1. He walked **slowly** to the car.
2. We have to get up early **tomorrow**.
3. The team **quickly** ran around the field.
4. My sister sings **beautifully**.
5. His friend is **very** considerate of others.

tomorrow
beautifully
slowly
quickly
very

Writing Practice: You've won a contest and you are on your way to the moon. Write a paragraph about your adventures.

©Teacher Created Materials, Inc.   11   #3302 Daily Skills Practice—Grades 4–5

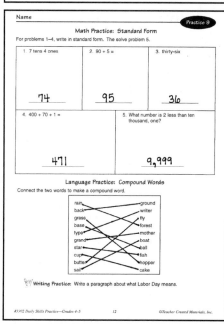

Name

Math Practice: Standard Form — Practice 9

For problems 1–4, write in standard form. The solve problem 5.

1. 7 tens 4 ones	2. 90 + 5 =	3. thirty-six
74	95	36

4. 400 + 70 + 1 =	5. What number is 2 less than ten thousand, one?
471	9,999

Language Practice: Compound Words

Connect the two words to make a compound word.

rain — ground
back — writer
grass — fly
base — forest
type — mother
grand — boat
star — ball
cup — fish
butter — hopper
sail — cake

Writing Practice: Write a paragraph about what Labor Day means.

#3302 Daily Skills Practice—Grades 4–5   12   ©Teacher Created Materials, Inc.

Name

Math Practice: Rounding — Practice 10

Round to the nearest 100. Then solve problem 5.

1. 864	2. 729	3. 671
900	700	700

4. 5,329	5. Greta is 6 years younger than her brother. Her brother is 13. How old is Greta?
5,300	7 years old

Language Practice: Contractions

Circle the correct contraction for each sentence.

1. We (**won't**, willn't) arrive at school late.
2. The food (**wasn't**, was'nt) cooked properly.
3. They (hav'nt, **haven't**) done their chores this week.
4. (I'ave, **I've**) seen a meteor fall from the sky.
5. It looks like (**it's**, its') going to rain.

Writing Practice: Write about your favorite foods. What are they, and why do you like them? Then draw a picture of them.

©Teacher Created Materials, Inc.   13   #3302 Daily Skills Practice—Grades 4–5

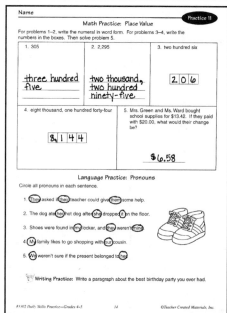

Name

Math Practice: Place Value — Practice 11

For problems 1–2, write the numeral in word form. For problems 3–4, write the numbers in the boxes. Then solve problem 5.

1. 305	2. 2,295	3. two hundred six
three hundred five	two thousand, two hundred ninety-five.	2 0 6

4. eight thousand, one hundred forty-four	5. Mrs. Green and Ms. Ward bought school supplies for $13.42. If they paid with $20.00, what would their change be?
8 1 4 4	$6.58

Language Practice: Pronouns

Circle all pronouns in each sentence.

1. (They) asked if (their) teacher could give (them) some help.
2. The dog ate (her) hot dog after (she) dropped (it) on the floor.
3. Shoes were found in (my) locker, and (they) weren't (mine).
4. (My) family likes to go shopping with (our) cousin.
5. (We) weren't sure if the present belonged to (her).

Writing Practice: Write a paragraph about the best birthday party you ever had.

#3302 Daily Skills Practice—Grades 4–5   14   ©Teacher Created Materials, Inc.

Name

Math Practice: Number Sentences — Practice 12

Write a number sentence for each word problem. Then solve.

1. The judges ordered 28 ribbons and 32 trophies for the contest. How many prizes were ordered?	2. A circus has 7 clowns, 3 monkeys, and 6 tigers. How many are in the circus in all?	3. Joy baked 12 cookies. She gave 7 cookies to a friend. How many cookies are left for her?
28 + 32 = 60	7 + 3 + 6 = 16	12 − 7 = 5
60 prizes	16 in all	5 cookies

4. Todd has 8 stamps. On Friday his brother got 15. How many more stamps does Todd's brother have?	5. Kenya had 3 basketballs, 2 footballs, 1 soccer ball, and 5 baseballs. How many balls did he have in all?
15 − 8 = 7	3 + 2 + 1 + 5 = 11
7 stamps	11 balls

Language Practice: Common and Proper Nouns

Write **C** for *common* and **P** for *proper* nouns.

C 1. house
P 2. White House
P 3. Jill
C 4. sister
C 5. state

P 6. Missouri
C 7. toy store
C 8. store
C 9. deer
P 10. Deerfield St.

Writing Practice: Write a paragraph explaining what it means when someone says "beauty is only skin deep." Then tell about someone you think is beautiful inside.

©Teacher Created Materials, Inc.   15   #3302 Daily Skills Practice—Grades 4–5

Page 16

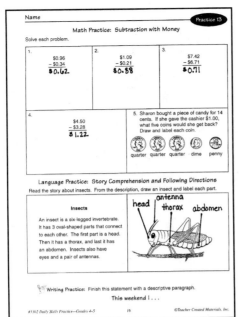

Math Practice: Subtraction with Money

Solve each problem.

1.	2.	3.
$0.96 − $0.34 = **$0.62**	$1.09 − $0.21 = **$0.88**	$7.42 − $6.71 = **$0.71**

4.	5. Sharon bought a piece of candy for 14 cents. If she gave the cashier $1.00, what five coins would she get back? Draw and label each coin.
$4.50 − $3.28 = **$1.22**	quarter quarter quarter dime penny

Language Practice: Story Comprehension and Following Directions
Read the story about insects. From the description, draw an insect and label each part.

Insects
An insect is a six-legged invertebrate. It has 3 oval-shaped parts that connect to each other. The first part is a head. Then it has a thorax, and last it has an abdomen. Insects also have eyes and a pair of antennas.

Writing Practice: Finish this statement with a descriptive paragraph.
This weekend I . . .

#3302 Daily Skills Practice—Grades 4–5 16 ©Teacher Created Materials, Inc.

Page 17

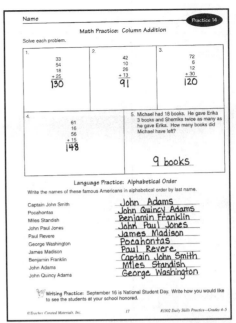

Math Practice: Column Addition

Solve each problem.

1.	2.	3.
33 54 18 + 25 = **130**	42 10 26 + 13 = **91**	72 6 12 + 30 = **120**

4.	5. Michael had 18 books. He gave Erika 3 books and Shemika twice as many as he gave Erika. How many books did Michael have left?
61 16 56 + 15 = **148**	**9 books**

Language Practice: Alphabetical Order
Write the names of these famous Americans in alphabetical order by last name.

Captain John Smith
Pocahontas
Miles Standish
John Paul Jones
Paul Revere
George Washington
James Madison
Benjamin Franklin
John Adams
John Quincy Adams

John Adams
John Quincy Adams
Benjamin Franklin
John Paul Jones
James Madison
Pocahontas
Paul Revere
Captain John Smith
Miles Standish
George Washington

Writing Practice: September 16 is National Student Day. Write how you would like to see the students at your school honored.

©Teacher Created Materials, Inc. 17 #3302 Daily Skills Practice—Grades 4–5

Page 18

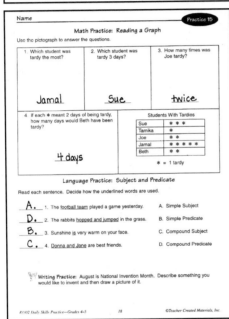

Math Practice: Reading a Graph
Use the pictograph to answer the questions.

1. Which student was tardy the most?	2. Which student was tardy 3 days?	3. How many times was Joe tardy?
Jamal	**Sue**	**twice**

4. If each ✱ meant 2 days of being tardy, how many days would Beth have been tardy?	Students With Tardies
4 days	Sue ✱✱✱ / Tamika ✱ / Joe ✱✱ / Jamal ✱✱✱✱✱ / Beth ✱✱ ✱ = 1 tardy

Language Practice: Subject and Predicate

Read each sentence. Decide how the underlined words are used.

A. 1. The football team played a game yesterday. A. Simple Subject
D. 2. The rabbits hopped and jumped in the grass. B. Simple Predicate
B. 3. Sunshine is very warm on your face. C. Compound Subject
C. 4. Donna and Jane are best friends. D. Compound Predicate

Writing Practice: August is National Invention Month. Describe something you would like to invent and then draw a picture of it.

#3302 Daily Skills Practice—Grades 4–5 18 ©Teacher Created Materials, Inc.

Page 19

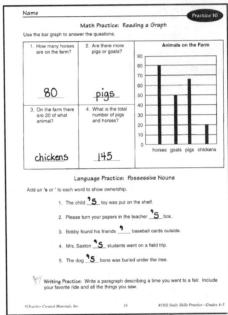

Math Practice: Reading a Graph
Use the bar graph to answer the questions.

1. How many horses are on the farm?	2. Are there more pigs or goats?	Animals on the Farm
80	**pigs**	(bar graph: horses goats pigs chickens)

3. On the farm there are 20 of what animal?	4. What is the total number of pigs and horses?
chickens	**145**

Language Practice: Possessive Nouns

Add an 's or ' to each word to show ownership.

1. The child**'s** toy was put on the shelf.
2. Please turn your papers in the teacher**'s** box.
3. Bobby found his friends**'** baseball cards outside.
4. Mrs. Saxton**'s** students went on a field trip.
5. The dog**'s** bone was buried under the tree.

Writing Practice: Write a paragraph describing a time you went to a fair. Include your favorite ride and all the things you saw.

©Teacher Created Materials, Inc. 19 #3302 Daily Skills Practice—Grades 4–5

Page 20

Math Practice: Place Value
For problems 1–4, find what number value is represented by the 7. Then solve problem 5.

1. 76	2. 927	3. 7,253
70	**7**	**7,000**

4. 6,745	5. Sherwon had 38 baseball cards. He gave 10 to Antwone. How many cards does Sherwon have left?
700	**28 cards**

Language Practice: Sentence Fragments
Finish each fragment to make complete sentences. (Answers will vary.)

1. Jose came to _____
2. Watch out for _____
3. _____ finished the race.
4. _____ comes down the road.
5. An ugly bug _____
6. _____ is pink with green stripes.

Writing Practice: During holidays students get some extra days off from school. Write a paragraph about things you will do on your days off from school.

#3302 Daily Skills Practice—Grades 4–5 20 ©Teacher Created Materials, Inc.

Page 21

Math Practice: Place Value
For problems 1–2, write the numbers in the boxes. For problems 3–4, write the numeral in word form. Then solve problem 5.

1. fifteen thousand, seventy-two	2. three hundred thirty thousand, one hundred two	3. 888
1 5 , 0 7 2	**3 3 0 , 1 0 2**	**eight hundred eighty-eight**

4. 4.236	5. Using the number of boys and girls in your class, write a number sentence showing how many students are in your class.
four and two hundred thirty-six thousandths	**Answers will vary.**

Language Practice: Sentences
Rewrite the paragraph with complete sentences. Remember to add correct end marks and capital letters.

During school today we had a test the test was in social studies we had to write the capital of each state I got two answers wrong the capital of Missouri is Springfield, not St. Louis, the capital of California is Sacramento, not Los Angeles.

During school today we had a test. The test was in social studies. We had to write the capital of each state. I got two answers wrong. The capital of Missouri is Springfield, not St. Louis. The capital of California is Sacramento, not Los Angeles.

Writing Practice: Pretend you are a meteorologist for a television station. Write a weather forecast for the news by how it looks outside today.

©Teacher Created Materials, Inc. 21 #3302 Daily Skills Practice—Grades 4–5

Page 22

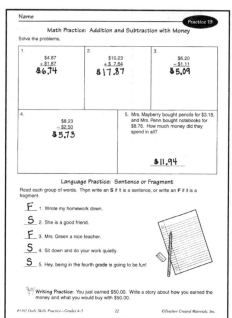

Name _____

Math Practice: Addition and Subtraction with Money

Solve the problems.

| 1. $4.87 + $1.87 = **$6.74** | 2. $10.23 + $ 7.64 = **$17.87** | 3. $6.20 − $1.11 = **$5.09** |

4. $8.23 − $2.50 = **$5.73**

5. Mrs. Mayberry bought pencils for $3.18, and Mrs. Penn bought notebooks for $8.76. How much money did they spend in all?

$11.94

Language Practice: Sentence or Fragment

Read each group of words. Then write an **S** if it is a sentence, or write an **F** if it is a fragment.

F 1. Wrote my homework down.
S 2. She is a good friend.
F 3. Mrs. Green a nice teacher.
S 4. Sit down and do your work quietly.
S 5. Hey, being in the fourth grade is going to be fun!

✍ Writing Practice: You just earned $50.00. Write a story about how you earned the money and what you would buy with $50.00.

Page 23

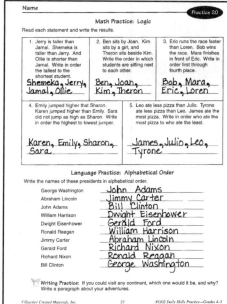

Name _____

Math Practice: Logic

Read each statement and write the results.

1. Jerry is taller than Jamal. Shemeka is taller than Jerry. And Ollie is shorter than Jamal. Write in order the tallest to the shortest student.

Shemeka, Jerry, Jamal, Ollie

2. Ben sits by Joan. Kim sits by a girl, and Theron sits beside Kim. Write the order in which students are sitting next to each other.

Ben, Joan, Kim, Theron

3. Eric runs the race faster than Loren. Bob wins the race. Mara finishes in front of Eric. Write in order first through fourth place.

Bob, Mara, Eric, Loren

4. Emily jumped higher that Sharon. Karen jumped higher than Emily. Sara did not jump as high as Sharon. Write in order the highest to lowest jumper.

Karen, Emily, Sharon, Sara

5. Leo ate less pizza than Julio. Tyrone ate less pizza than Leo. James ate the most pizza. Write in order who ate the most pizza to who ate the least.

James, Julio, Leo, Tyrone

Language Practice: Alphabetical Order

Write the names of these presidents in alphabetical order.

George Washington	John Adams
Abraham Lincoln	Jimmy Carter
John Adams	Bill Clinton
William Harrison	Dwight Eisenhower
Dwight Eisenhower	Gerald Ford
Ronald Reagan	William Harrison
Jimmy Carter	Abraham Lincoln
Gerald Ford	Richard Nixon
Richard Nixon	Ronald Reagan
Bill Clinton	George Washington

✍ Writing Practice: If you could visit any continent, which one would it be, and why? Write a paragraph about your adventures.

Page 24

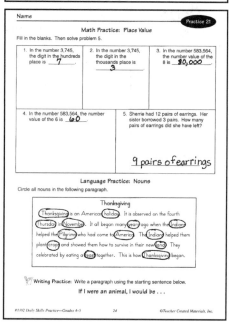

Name _____

Math Practice: Place Value

Fill in the blanks. Then solve problem 5.

1. In the number 3,745, the digit in the hundreds place is **7**.
2. In the number 3,745, the digit in the thousands place is **3**.
3. In the number 583,564, the number value of the 8 is **80,000**.
4. In the number 583,564, the number value of the 6 is **60**.
5. Sherrie had 12 pairs of earrings. Her sister borrowed 3 pairs. How many pairs of earrings did she have left?

9 pairs of earrings

Language Practice: Nouns

Circle all nouns in the following paragraph.

Thanksgiving

(Thanksgiving) is an American (holiday). It is observed on the fourth (Thursday) in (November). It all began many (years) ago when the (Indians) helped the (Pilgrims) who had come to (America). The (Indians) helped them plant (crops) and showed them how to survive in their new (land). They celebrated by eating a (feast) together. This is how (Thanksgiving) began.

✍ Writing Practice: Write a paragraph using the starting sentence below.

If I were an animal, I would be . . .

Page 25

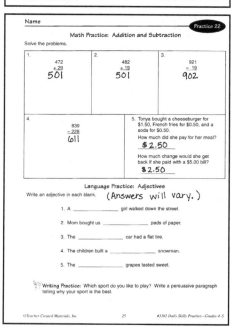

Name _____

Math Practice: Addition and Subtraction

Solve the problems.

| 1. 472 + 29 = **501** | 2. 482 + 19 = **501** | 3. 921 − 19 = **902** |

4. 839 − 228 = **611**

5. Tonya bought a cheeseburger for $1.50, French fries for $0.50, and a soda for $0.50.

How much did she pay for her meal?
$2.50

How much change would she get back if she paid with a $5.00 bill?
$2.50

Language Practice: Adjectives

Write an adjective in each blank. (Answers will vary.)

1. A _____ girl walked down the street.
2. Mom bought us _____ pads of paper.
3. The _____ car had a flat tire.
4. The children built a _____ snowman.
5. The _____ grapes tasted sweet.

✍ Writing Practice: Which sport do you like to play? Write a persuasive paragraph telling why your sport is the best.

Page 26

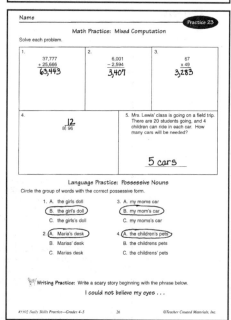

Name _____

Math Practice: Mixed Computation

Solve each problem.

| 1. 37,777 + 25,666 = **63,443** | 2. 6,001 − 2,594 = **3,407** | 3. 67 × 49 = **3,283** |

4. **12** ← 8)96

5. Mrs. Lewis' class is going on a field trip. There are 20 students going, and 4 children can ride in each car. How many cars will be needed?

5 cars

Language Practice: Possessive Nouns

Circle the group of words with the correct possessive form.

1. A. the girls doll
   B. the girl's doll
   C. the girls's doll
2. **A. Maria's desk**
   B. Marias' desk
   C. Marias desk
3. A. my moms car
   B. my mom's car
   C. my moms's car
4. **A. the children's pets**
   B. the childrens pets
   C. the childrens' pets

✍ Writing Practice: Write a scary story beginning with the phrase below.

I could not believe my eyes . . .

Page 27

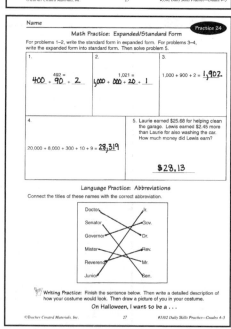

Name _____

Math Practice: Expanded/Standard Form

For problems 1–2, write the standard form in expanded form. For problems 3–4, write the expanded form into standard form. Then solve problem 5.

1. 492 = **400 + 90 + 2**
2. 1,021 = **1,000 + 000 + 20 + 1**
3. 1,000 + 900 + 2 = **1,902**
4. 20,000 + 8,000 + 300 + 10 + 9 = **28,319**
5. Laurie earned $25.68 for helping clean the garage. Lewis earned $2.45 more than Laurie for also washing the car. How much money did Lewis earn?

$28.13

Language Practice: Abbreviations

Connect the titles of these names with the correct abbreviation.

Doctor	Jr.
Senator	Gov.
Governor	Dr.
Mister	Rev.
Reverend	Mr.
Junior	Sen.

✍ Writing Practice: Finish the sentence below. Then write a detailed description of how your costume would look. Then draw a picture of you in your costume.

On Halloween, I want to be a . . .

Page 28

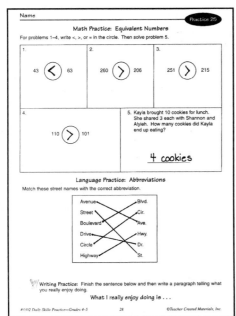

Page 29

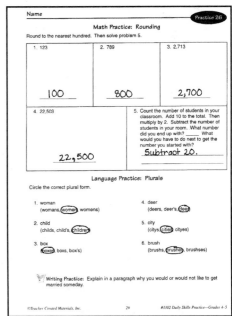

Page 30

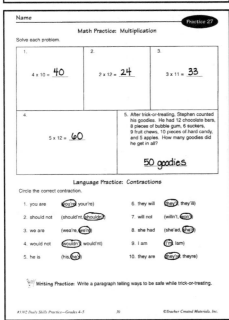

Page 31

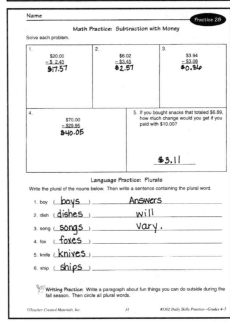

Page 32

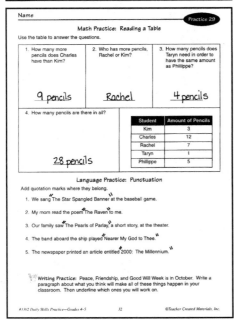

Page 33

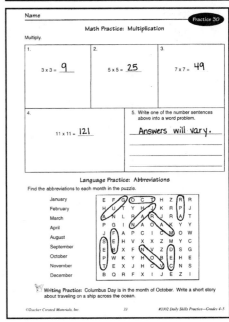

Page 34

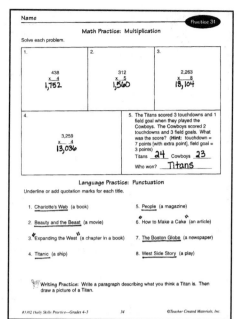

Name

Practice 31

Math Practice: Multiplication

Solve each problem.

1.	2.	3.
438 x 4 1,752	312 x 5 1,560	2,263 x 8 18,104

4.	5. The Titans scored 3 touchdowns and 1 field goal when they played the Cowboys. The Cowboys scored 2 touchdowns and 3 field goals. What was the score? (**Hint:** touchdown = 7 points [with extra point], field goal = 3 points)
3,259 x 4 13,036	Titans 24 Cowboys 23 Who won? Titans

Language Practice: Punctuation

Underline or add quotation marks for each title.

1. Charlotte's Web (a book)
2. Beauty and the Beast (a movie)
3. "Expanding the West" (a chapter in a book)
4. Titanic (a ship)
5. People (a magazine)
6. "How to Make a Cake" (an article)
7. The Boston Globe (a newspaper)
8. West Side Story (a play)

✏️ **Writing Practice:** Write a paragraph describing what you think a Titan is. Then draw a picture of a Titan.

#3302 Daily Skills Practice—Grades 4–5   34   ©Teacher Created Materials, Inc.

Page 35

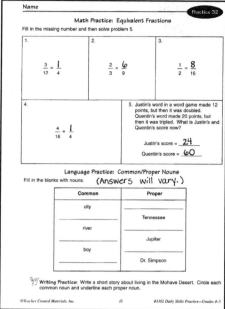

Name

Practice 32

Math Practice: Equivalent Fractions

Fill in the missing number and then solve problem 5.

1.	2.	3.
$\frac{3}{12} = \frac{1}{4}$	$\frac{2}{3} = \frac{6}{9}$	$\frac{1}{2} = \frac{8}{16}$

4.	5. Justin's word in a word game made 12 points, but then it was doubled. Quentin's word made 20 points, but then it was tripled. What is Justin's and Quentin's score now?
$\frac{4}{16} = \frac{1}{4}$	Justin's score = 24 Quentin's score = 60

Language Practice: Common/Proper Nouns

Fill in the blanks with nouns.   (Answers will vary.)

Common	Proper
city	
	Tennessee
river	
	Jupiter
boy	
	Dr. Simpson

✏️ **Writing Practice:** Write a short story about living in the Mohave Desert. Circle each common noun and underline each proper noun.

©Teacher Created Materials, Inc.   35   #3302 Daily Skills Practice—Grades 4–5

Page 36

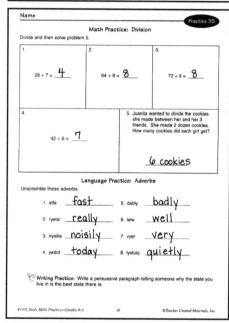

Name

Practice 33

Math Practice: Division

Divide and then solve problem 5.

1.	2.	3.
28 ÷ 7 = 4	64 ÷ 8 = 8	72 ÷ 9 = 8

4.	5. Juanita wanted to divide the cookies she made between her and her 3 friends. She made 2 dozen cookies. How many cookies did each girl get?
42 ÷ 6 = 7	6 cookies

Language Practice: Adverbs

Unscramble these adverbs.

1. stfa fast
2. ryelal really
3. nyoilis noisily
4. yadot today
5. dably badly
6. lelw well
7. vyer very
8. lyetuiq quietly

✏️ **Writing Practice:** Write a persuasive paragraph telling someone why the state you live in is the best state there is.

#3302 Daily Skills Practice—Grades 4–5   36   ©Teacher Created Materials, Inc.

Page 37

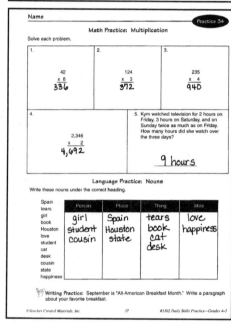

Name

Practice 34

Math Practice: Multiplication

Solve each problem.

1.	2.	3.
42 x 8 336	124 x 3 372	235 x 4 940

4.	5. Kym watched television for 2 hours on Friday, 3 hours on Saturday, and on Sunday twice as much as on Friday. How many hours did she watch over the three days?
2,346 x 2 4,692	9 hours

Language Practice: Nouns

Write these nouns under the correct heading.

Spain, tears, girl, book, Houston, love, student, cat, desk, cousin, state, happiness

Person	Place	Thing	Idea
girl	Spain	tears	love
student	Houston	book	happiness
cousin	state	cat	
		desk	

✏️ **Writing Practice:** September is "All-American Breakfast Month." Write a paragraph about your favorite breakfast.

©Teacher Created Materials, Inc.   37   #3302 Daily Skills Practice—Grades 4–5

Page 38

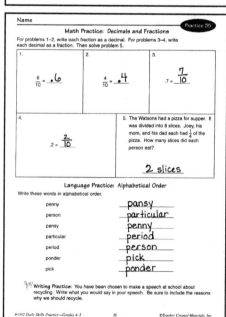

Name

Practice 35

Math Practice: Decimals and Fractions

For problems 1–2, write each fraction as a decimal. For problems 3–4, write each decimal as a fraction. Then solve problem 5.

1.	2.	3.
$\frac{6}{10} = .6$	$\frac{4}{10} = .4$	$.7 = \frac{7}{10}$

4.	5. The Watsons had a pizza for supper. It was divided into 8 slices. Joey, his mom, and his dad each had $\frac{1}{4}$ of the pizza. How many slices did each person eat?
$.2 = \frac{2}{10}$	2 slices

Language Practice: Alphabetical Order

Write these words in alphabetical order.

penny	pansy
person	particular
pansy	penny
particular	period
period	person
ponder	pick
pick	ponder

✏️ **Writing Practice:** You have been chosen to make a speech at school about recycling. Write what you would say in your speech. Be sure to include the reasons why we should recycle.

#3302 Daily Skills Practice—Grades 4–5   38   ©Teacher Created Materials, Inc.

Page 39

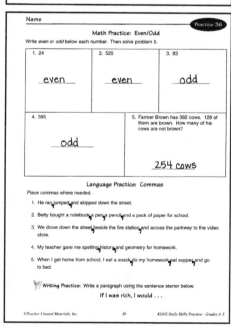

Name

Practice 36

Math Practice: Even/Odd

Write even or odd below each number. Then solve problem 5.

1. 24	2. 520	3. 83
even	even	odd

4. 395	5. Farmer Brown has 382 cows. 128 of them are brown. How many of his cows are not brown?
odd	254 cows

Language Practice: Commas

Place commas where needed.

1. He ran, jumped, and skipped down the street.
2. Betty bought a notebook, a pen, a pencil, and a pack of paper for school.
3. We drove down the street, beside the fire station, and across the parkway to the video store.
4. My teacher gave me spelling, history, and geometry for homework.
5. When I get home from school, I eat a snack, do my homework, eat supper, and go to bed.

✏️ **Writing Practice:** Write a paragraph using the sentence starter below.

If I was rich, I would . . .

©Teacher Created Materials, Inc.   39   #3302 Daily Skills Practice—Grades 4–5

Page 40

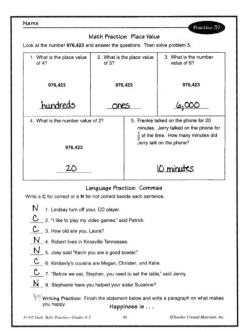

Name _____

Math Practice: Place Value

Look at the number **976,423** and answer the questions. Then solve problem 5.

1. What is the place value of 4?	2. What is the place value of 3?	3. What is the number value of 6?
976,423	976,423	976,423
hundreds	ones	6,000

4. What is the number value of 2?	5. Frankie talked on the phone for 20 minutes. Jerry talked on the phone for $\frac{1}{2}$ of the time. How many minutes did Jerry talk on the phone?
976,423	
20	10 minutes

Language Practice: Commas

Write a **C** for correct or a **N** for not correct beside each sentence.

N 1. Lindsay turn off your, CD player.
C 2. "I like to play my video games," said Patrick.
C 3. How old are you, Laura?
N 4. Robert lives in Knoxville Tennessee.
N 5. Joey said "Kevin you are a good bowler."
C 6. Kimberly's cousins are Megan, Christen, and Katie.
C 7. "Before we eat, Stephen, you need to set the table," said Jenny.
N 8. Stephanie have you helped your sister Suzanne?

Writing Practice: Finish the statement below and write a paragraph on what makes you happy.
Happiness is . . .

#3302 Daily Skills Practice—Grades 4–5   40   ©Teacher Created Materials, Inc.

Page 41

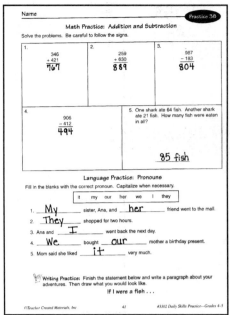

Name _____

Math Practice: Addition and Subtraction

Solve the problems. Be careful to follow the signs.

1. 346 + 421 = 767	2. 259 + 630 = 889	3. 987 − 183 = 804

4. 906 − 412 = 494	5. One shark ate 64 fish. Another shark ate 21 fish. How many fish were eaten in all? 85 fish

Language Practice: Pronouns

Fill in the blanks with the correct pronoun. Capitalize when necessary.

it   my   our   her   we   I   they

1. My sister, Ana, and her friend went to the mall.
2. They shopped for two hours.
3. Ana and I went back the next day.
4. We bought our mother a birthday present.
5. Mom said she liked it very much.

Writing Practice: Finish the statement below and write a paragraph about your adventures. Then draw what you would look like.
If I were a fish . . .

©Teacher Created Materials, Inc.   41   #3302 Daily Skills Practice—Grades 4–5

Page 42

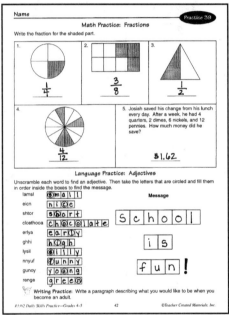

Name _____

Math Practice: Fractions

Write the fraction for the shaded part.

1. $\frac{}{4}$	2. $\frac{3}{8}$	3. $\frac{1}{2}$

4. $\frac{4}{12}$	5. Josiah saved his change from his lunch every day. After a week, he had 4 quarters, 2 dimes, 6 nickels, and 12 pennies. How much money did he save? $1.62

Language Practice: Adjectives

Unscramble each word to find an adjective. Then take the letters that are circled and fill them in order inside the boxes to find the message.

lsml — small
eicn — nice
shtor — short
clcethooa — chocolate
erlya — early
ghhi — high
lysil — silly
nnyuf — funny
gunoy — young
renge — green

Message: School is fun!

Writing Practice: Write a paragraph describing what you would like to be when you become an adult.

#3302 Daily Skills Practice—Grades 4–5   42   ©Teacher Created Materials, Inc.

Page 43

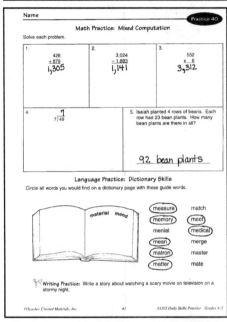

Name _____

Math Practice: Mixed Computation

Solve each problem.

1. 426 + 879 = 1,305	2. 3,024 − 1,883 = 1,141	3. 552 x 6 = 3,312

4. 7 ÷ 49 = 7	5. Isaiah planted 4 rows of beans. Each row has 23 bean plants. How many bean plants are there in all? 92 bean plants

Language Practice: Dictionary Skills

Circle all words you would find on a dictionary page with these guide words.

material mend

measure   match
memory   meet
menial   medical
mean   merge
matron   master
matter   mate

Writing Practice: Write a story about watching a scary movie on television on a stormy night.

©Teacher Created Materials, Inc.   43   #3302 Daily Skills Practice—Grades 4–5

Page 44

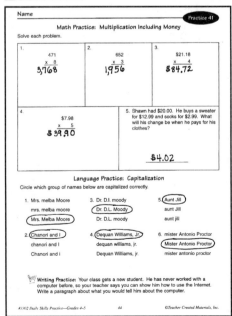

Name _____

Math Practice: Multiplication Including Money

Solve each problem.

1. 471 x 8 = 3,768	2. 652 x 3 = 1,956	3. $21.18 x 4 = $84.72

4. $7.98 x 5 = $39.90	5. Shawn had $20.00. He buys a sweater for $12.99 and socks for $2.99. What will his change be when he pays for his clothes? $4.02

Language Practice: Capitalization

Circle which group of names below are capitalized correctly.

1. Mrs. melba Moore
   mrs. melba moore
   Mrs. Melba Moore

2. **Chanori and I**
   chanori and I
   Chanori and i

3. Dr. D.l. moody
   Dr. D.L. Moody
   Dr. D.L. moody

4. **Dequan Williams, Jr.**
   dequan williams, jr.
   Dequan Williams, jr.

5. **Aunt Jill**
   aunt Jill
   aunt jill

6. mister Antonio Proctor
   Mister Antonio Proctor
   mister antonio proctor

Writing Practice: Your class gets a new student. He has never worked with a computer before, so your teacher says you can show him how to use the Internet. Write a paragraph about what you would tell him about the computer.

#3302 Daily Skills Practice—Grades 4–5   44   ©Teacher Created Materials, Inc.

Page 45

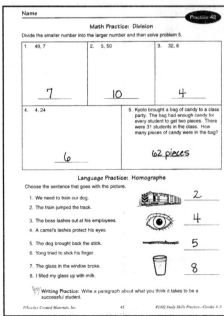

Name _____

Math Practice: Division

Divide the smaller number into the larger number and then solve problem 5.

1. 49, 7	2. 5, 50	3. 32, 8
7	10	4

4. 4, 24	5. Kyoto brought a bag of candy to a class party. The bag had enough candy for every student to get two pieces. There were 31 students in the class. How many pieces of candy were in the bag?
6	62 pieces

Language Practice: Homographs

Choose the sentence that goes with the picture.

1. We need to train our dog.
2. The train jumped the track.   2
3. The boss lashes out at his employees.
4. A camel's lashes protect his eyes.   4
5. The dog brought back the stick.
6. Yong tried to stick his finger.   5
7. The glass in the window broke.
8. I filled my glass up with milk.   8

Writing Practice: Write a paragraph about what you think it takes to be a successful student.

©Teacher Created Materials, Inc.   45   #3302 Daily Skills Practice—Grades 4–5

Page 46

Practice 43

Math Practice: Fractions

Fill in the blanks with the missing number. Then solve problem 5.

1.	2.	3.
$\frac{1}{4} = \frac{4}{16}$	$\frac{3}{5} = \frac{12}{20}$	$\frac{5}{4} = \frac{20}{16}$

4.	5. Brittani had 13 goldfish. Her mother bought her 6 more. The next day one fish found 2 dead. Then a week later one fish had 12 babies. How many goldfish does she now have?
$\frac{2}{3} = \frac{8}{12}$	29 goldfish

Language Practice: Prefixes

Circle each word with a prefix.

happiness	(unclear)	(redone)
jumping	helpless	(preseason)
careful	mender	(disadvantage)
(misinterpret)	capable	(mistake)

✏ *Writing Practice:* Write a paragraph using the sentence starter below.

When I get home from school, I . . .

Page 47

Practice 44

Math Practice: Fractions

Write <, >, or = between each fraction and then solve problem 5.

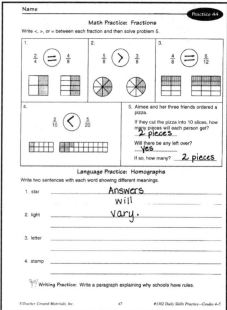

4.	5. Aimee and her three friends ordered a pizza.
$\frac{2}{10}$ (<) $\frac{5}{20}$	If they cut the pizza into 10 slices, how many pieces will each person get? __2 pieces__
	Will there be any left over? __Yes__
	If so, how many? __2 pieces__

Language Practice: Homographs

Write two sentences with each word showing different meanings.

1. star ___Answers___
2. light ___will___ ___vary.___
3. letter ___
4. stamp ___

✏ *Writing Practice:* Write a paragraph explaining why schools have rules.

Page 48

Practice 45

Math Practice: Rounding

Round to the place value that is underlined. Then solve number 5.

1. 6,789	2. 5,329	3. 982
6,800	5,330	980

4. 23,087	5. Roberto lives 134 miles from the nearest mountain. Round this distance to the nearest 10 miles.
23,000	130 miles

Language Practice: Suffixes

Underline each word that contains a suffix.

comfortable	foolish	uncover
unwrap	prepaid	teacher
argument	singer	election
laziness	finalist	jumping
prearrange	careless	beautiful

✏ *Writing Practice:* Write a story about the wildest dream you've ever had.

Page 49

Practice 46

Math Practice: Multiplication

Fill in the blanks. Then solve problem 5.

1.	2.	3.
__8__ x 3 = 24	4 x __2__ = 8	6 x __7__ = 42

4.	5. Darrell has 13 pencils. He gave 8 to Jorge. He then found enough pencils to double what he had left. How many pencils does Darrell have now?
__8__ x 9 = 72	10 pencils

Language Practice: Spelling

Circle the correctly spelled word.

1. (receive) recieve	5. wierd (weird)
2. (misspell) mispell	6. procede (proceed)
3. calender (calendar)	7. thier (their)
4. (vacuum) vaccum	8. (believe) beleive

✏ *Writing Practice:* Write a paragraph with the sentence starter below.

This weekend I had the most fun when . . .

Page 50

Practice 47

Math Practice: Multiplication

Solve each problem.

1.	2.	3.
34 x 6 = 204	65 x 5 = 325	123 x 4 = 492

4.	5. Sherry had 4 pairs of white socks, 5 pairs of black socks, and 6 pairs of brown socks.
456 x 2 = 912	How many pairs of socks did Sherry have? __15__
	Since a pair is two, count each sock. How many socks is that? __30__

Language Practice: Spelling

Rewrite each misspelled word correctly.

1. auther	author	6. tommorrow	tomorrow
2. frite	fright	7. twelth	twelfth
3. abcense	absence	8. suprise	surprise
4. certian	certain	9. cheif	chief
5. Wendesday	Wednesday	10. fourty	forty

✏ *Writing Practice:* Write a paragraph about the best birthday you ever had.

Page 51

Practice 48

Math Practice: Division

Solve each problem.

1.	2.	3.
$\frac{7}{2)14}$	$\frac{7\ r\ 1}{5)36}$	$\frac{12}{3)36}$

4.	5. Four buses were driven to school. There were 52 students on each bus. How many students were on all four buses?
$\frac{8\ r\ 4}{6)52}$	208 students

Language Practice: Homographs

Write two sentences with each homograph showing different meanings. Then think of one more homograph and write two sentences with it.

1. rose ___Answers___
___will___
2. leaves ___vary.___
3. ___

✏ *Writing Practice:* Write a story about visiting a farm and seeing farm animals up close.

Page 52

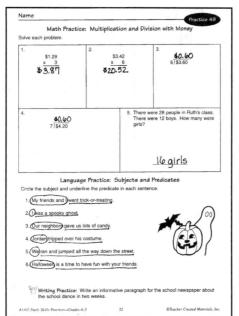

Practice 49

Math Practice: Multiplication and Division with Money

Solve each problem.

1. $1.29 ×3 **$3.87**	2. $3.42 ×6 **$20.52**	3. **$0.60** 6)$3.60

4. **$0.60** 7)$4.20	5. There were 28 people in Ruth's class. There were 12 boys. How many were girls? **16 girls**

Language Practice: Subjects and Predicates

Circle the subject and underline the predicate in each sentence.

1. (My friends and I) went trick-or-treating.
2. (I) was a spooky ghost.
3. (Our neighbor) gave us lots of candy.
4. (Jordan) tripped over his costume.
5. (We) ran and jumped all the way down the street.
6. (Halloween) is a time to have fun with your friends.

Writing Practice: Write an informative paragraph for the school newspaper about the school dance in two weeks.

#3302 Daily Skills Practice—Grades 4–5   52   ©Teacher Created Materials, Inc.

Page 53

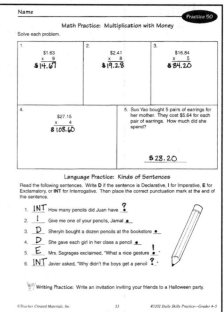

Practice 50

Math Practice: Multiplication with Money

Solve each problem.

1. $1.63 ×9 **$14.67**	2. $2.41 ×8 **$19.28**	3. $16.84 ×5 **$84.20**

4. $27.15 ×4 **$108.60**	5. Suo Yao bought 5 pairs of earrings for her mother. They cost $5.64 for each pair of earrings. How much did she spend? **$28.20**

Language Practice: Kinds of Sentences

Read the following sentences. Write D if the sentence is Declarative, I for Imperative, E for Exclamatory, or INT for Interrogative. Then place the correct punctuation mark at the end of the sentence.

1. **INT** How many pencils did Juan have **?**
2. **I** Give me one of your pencils, Jamal **.**
3. **D** Sherylin bought a dozen pencils at the bookstore **.**
4. **D** She gave each girl in her class a pencil **.**
5. **E** Mrs. Sagrages exclaimed, "What a nice gesture **!**
6. **INT** Javier asked, "Why didn't the boys get a pencil **?**

Writing Practice: Write an invitation inviting your friends to a Halloween party.

©Teacher Created Materials, Inc.   53   #3302 Daily Skills Practice—Grades 4–5

Page 54

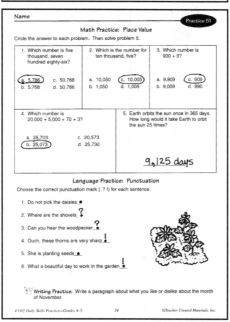

Practice 51

Math Practice: Place Value

Circle the answer to each problem. Then solve problem 5.

1. Which number is five thousand, seven hundred eighty-six? **a. 5,786** c. 50,768 b. 5,768 d. 50,786	2. Which is the number for ten thousand, five? a. 10,050 **c. 10,005** b. 1,050 d. 1,005	3. Which number is 900 + 9? a. 9,909 **c. 909** b. 9,009 d. 990

4. Which number is 20,000 + 5,000 + 70 + 3? a. 25,703 **b. 25,073** c. 20,573 d. 25,730	5. Earth orbits the sun once in 365 days. How long would it take Earth to orbit the sun 25 times? **9,125 days**

Language Practice: Punctuation

Choose the correct punctuation mark (. ? !) for each sentence.

1. Do not pick the daisies **.**
2. Where are the shovels **?**
3. Can you hear the woodpecker **?**
4. Ouch, these thorns are very sharp **!**
5. She is planting seeds **.**
6. What a beautiful day to work in the garden **!**

Writing Practice: Write a paragraph about what you like or dislike about the month of November.

#3302 Daily Skills Practice—Grades 4–5   54   ©Teacher Created Materials, Inc.

Page 55

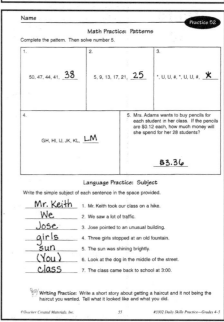

Practice 52

Math Practice: Patterns

Complete the pattern. Then solve number 5.

1. 50, 47, 44, 41, **38**	2. 5, 9, 13, 17, 21, **25**	3. *, U, U, #, *, U, U, #, **✳**

4. GH, HI, IJ, JK, KL, **LM**	5. Mrs. Adams wants to buy pencils for each student in her class. If the pencils are $0.12 each, how much money will she spend for her 28 students? **$3.36**

Language Practice: Subject

Write the simple subject of each sentence in the space provided.

Mr. Keith 1. Mr. Keith took our class on a hike.
We 2. We saw a lot of traffic.
Jose 3. Jose pointed to an unusual building.
girls 4. Three girls stopped at an old fountain.
sun 5. The sun was shining brightly.
(You) 6. Look at the dog in the middle of the street.
class 7. The class came back to school at 3:00.

Writing Practice: Write a short story about getting a haircut and it not being the haircut you wanted. Tell what it looked like and what you did.

©Teacher Created Materials, Inc.   55   #3302 Daily Skills Practice—Grades 4–5

Page 56

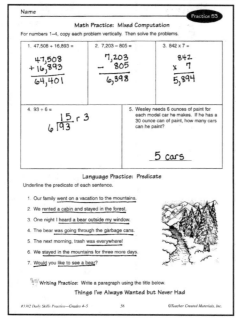

Practice 53

Math Practice: Mixed Computation

For numbers 1–4, copy each problem vertically. Then solve the problems.

1. 47,508 + 16,893 = 47,508 +16,893 **64,401**	2. 7,203 − 805 = 7,203 −805 **6,398**	3. 842 × 7 = 842 ×7 **5,894**

4. 93 ÷ 6 = **15 r 3** 6)93	5. Wesley needs 6 ounces of paint for each model car he makes. If he has a 30 ounce can of paint, how many cars can he paint? **5 cars**

Language Practice: Predicate

Underline the predicate of each sentence.

1. Our family went on a vacation to the mountains.
2. We rented a cabin and stayed in the forest.
3. One night I heard a bear outside my window.
4. The bear was going through the garbage cans.
5. The next morning, trash was everywhere!
6. We stayed in the mountains for three more days.
7. Would you like to see a bear?

Writing Practice: Write a paragraph using the title below.

Things I've Always Wanted but Never Had

#3302 Daily Skills Practice—Grades 4–5   56   ©Teacher Created Materials, Inc.

Page 57

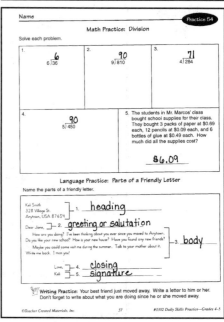

Practice 54

Math Practice: Division

Solve each problem.

1. **6** 6)36	2. **90** 9)810	3. **71** 4)284

4. **90** 5)450	5. The students in Mr. Marcos' class bought school supplies for their class. They bought 3 packs of paper at $0.69 each, 12 pencils at $0.09 each, and 6 bottles of glue at $0.49 each. How much did all the supplies cost? **$6.09**

Language Practice: Parts of a Friendly Letter

Name the parts of a friendly letter.

Keli Smith
328 Village St.
Anytown, USA 87654 } 1. **heading**

Dear Jane, 2. **greeting or salutation**

How are you doing? I've been thinking about you ever since you moved to Anytown. Do you like your new school? How is your new house? Have you found any new friends? Maybe you could come visit me during the summer. Talk to your mother about it. Write me back. I miss you! } 3. **body**

Love, 4. **closing**
Keli 5. **signature**

Writing Practice: Your best friend just moved away. Write a letter to him or her. Don't forget to write about what you are doing since he or she moved away.

©Teacher Created Materials, Inc.   57   #3302 Daily Skills Practice—Grades 4–5

Page 58

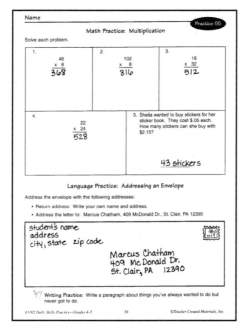

Page 59

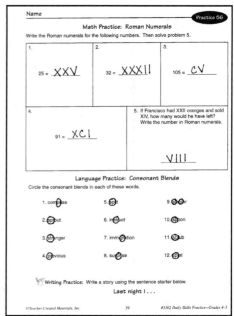

Page 60

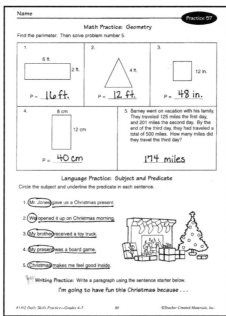

Page 61

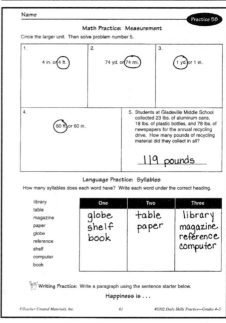

Page 62

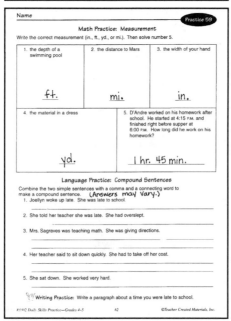

Page 63

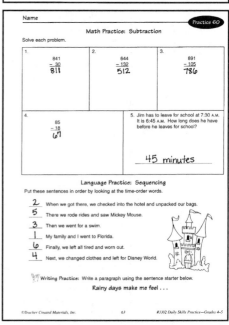

Page 64

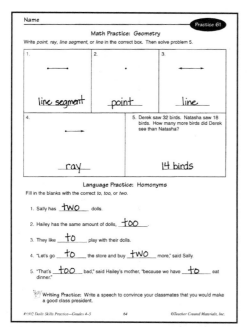

Practice 61

Math Practice: Geometry

Write *point, ray, line segment,* or *line* in the correct box. Then solve problem 5.

1. line segment	2. point	3. line
4. ray	5. Derek saw 32 birds. Natasha saw 18 birds. How many more birds did Derek see than Natasha? 14 birds	

Language Practice: Homonyms

Fill in the blanks with the correct *to, too,* or *two.*

1. Sally has __two__ dolls.

2. Hailey has the same amount of dolls, __too__.

3. They like __to__ play with their dolls.

4. "Let's go __to__ the store and buy __two__ more," said Sally.

5. "That's __too__ bad," said Hailey's mother, "because we have __to__ eat dinner."

Writing Practice: Write a speech to convince your classmates that you would make a good class president.

#3302 Daily Skills Practice—Grades 4–5   64   ©Teacher Created Materials, Inc.

Page 65

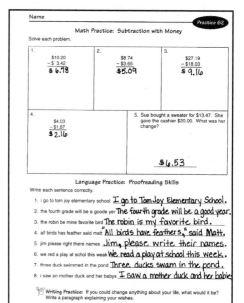

Practice 62

Math Practice: Subtraction with Money

Solve each problem.

1. $10.20 − $ 3.42 = $6.78	2. $8.74 − $3.65 = $5.09	3. $27.19 − $18.03 = $ 9.16
4. $4.03 − $1.87 = $2.16	5. Sue bought a sweater for $13.47. She gave the cashier $20.00. What was her change? $6.53	

Language Practice: Proofreading Skills

Write each sentence correctly.

1. i go to tom joy elementary school   I go to Tom Joy Elementary School.

2. the fourth grade will be a goode yer   The fourth grade will be a good year.

3. the robin is mine favorite bird   The robin is my favorite bird.

4. all birds has feather said matt   "All birds have feathers," said Matt.

5. jim please right there names   Jim, please write their names.

6. we red a play at schol this weak   We read a play at school this week.

7. three duck swimmed in the pond   Three ducks swam in the pond.

8. i saw a mother duck and her babys   I saw a mother duck and her babies.

Writing Practice: If you could change anything about your life, what would it be? Write a paragraph explaining your wishes.

©Teacher Created Materials, Inc.   65   #3302 Daily Skills Practice—Grades 4–5

Page 66

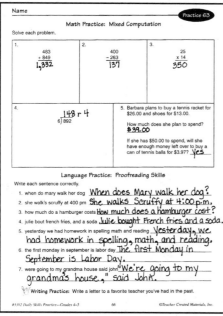

Practice 63

Math Practice: Mixed Computation

Solve each problem.

1. 483 + 849 = 1,332	2. 400 − 263 = 137	3. 25 x 14 = 350
4. 6) 892 = 148 r 4	5. Barbara plans to buy a tennis racket for $26.00 and shoes for $13.00. How much does she plan to spend? $39.00 If she has $50.00 to spend, will she have enough money left over to buy a can of tennis balls for $3.97? Yes	

Language Practice: Proofreading Skills

Write each sentence correctly.

1. when do mary walk her dog   When does Mary walk her dog?

2. she walk's scruffy at 400 pm   She walks Scruffy at 4:00 p.m.

3. how much do a hamburger costs   How much does a hamburger cost?

4. julie bout french fries, and a soda   Julie bought French fries and a soda.

5. yesterday we had homework in spelling math and reading   Yesterday, we had homework in spelling, math, and reading.

6. the first monday in september is labor day   The first Monday in September is Labor Day.

7. were going to my grandma house said john   "We're going to my grandma's house," said John.

Writing Practice: Write a letter to a favorite teacher you've had in the past.

#3302 Daily Skills Practice—Grades 4–5   66   ©Teacher Created Materials, Inc.

Page 67

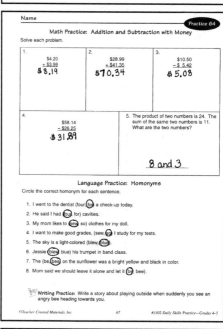

Practice 64

Math Practice: Addition and Subtraction with Money

Solve each problem.

1. $4.20 + $3.99 = $8.19	2. $28.99 + $41.35 = $70.34	3. $10.50 − $ 5.42 = $5.08
4. $58.14 − $26.25 = $ 31.89	5. The product of two numbers is 24. The sum of the same two numbers is 11. What are the two numbers? 8 and 3	

Language Practice: Homonyms

Circle the correct homonym for each sentence.

1. I went to the dentist (four, (for)) a check-up today.

2. He said I had (four), for) cavities.

3. My mom likes to (sew), so) clothes for my doll.

4. I want to make good grades, (sew, (so)) I study for my tests.

5. The sky is a light-colored (blew, (blue)).

6. Jessie (blew) blue) his trumpet in band class.

7. The (be, (bee)) on the sunflower was a bright yellow and black in color.

8. Mom said we should leave it alone and let it (be), bee).

Writing Practice: Write a story about playing outside when suddenly you see an angry bee heading towards you.

©Teacher Created Materials, Inc.   67   #3302 Daily Skills Practice—Grades 4–5

Page 68

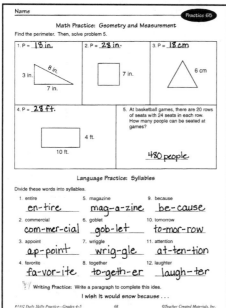

Practice 65

Math Practice: Geometry and Measurement

Find the perimeter. Then, solve problem 5.

1. P = 18 in.	2. P = 28 in.	3. P = 18 cm
4. P = 28 ft.	5. At basketball games, there are 20 rows of seats with 24 seats in each row. How many people can be seated at games? 480 people	

Language Practice: Syllables

Divide these words into syllables.

1. entire en-tire	5. magazine mag-a-zine	9. because be-cause
2. commercial com-mer-cial	6. goblet gob-let	10. tomorrow to-mor-row
3. appoint ap-point	7. wriggle wrig-gle	11. attention at-ten-tion
4. favorite fa-vor-ite	8. together to-geth-er	12. laughter laugh-ter

Writing Practice: Write a paragraph to complete this idea.

I wish it would snow because . . .

#3302 Daily Skills Practice—Grades 4–5   68   ©Teacher Created Materials, Inc.

Page 69

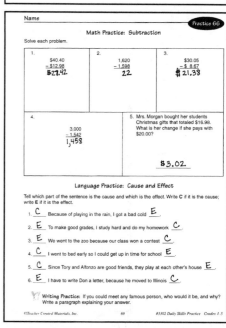

Practice 66

Math Practice: Subtraction

Solve each problem.

1. $40.40 − $12.98 = $27.42	2. 1,620 − 1,598 = 22	3. $30.05 − $ 8.67 = $ 21.38
4. 3,000 − 1,542 = 1,458	5. Mrs. Morgan bought her students Christmas gifts that totaled $16.98. What is her change if she pays with $20.00? $3.02	

Language Practice: Cause and Effect

Tell which part of the sentence is the cause and which is the effect. Write **C** if it is the cause; write **E** if it is the effect.

1. __C__ Because of playing in the rain, I got a bad cold __E__.

2. __E__ To make good grades, I study hard and do my homework __C__.

3. __E__ We went to the zoo because our class won a contest __C__.

4. __C__ I went to bed early so I could get up in time for school __E__.

5. __C__ Since Tory and Alfonzo are good friends, they play at each other's house __E__.

6. __E__ I have to write Don a letter, because he moved to Illinois __C__.

Writing Practice: If you could meet any famous person, who would it be, and why? Write a paragraph explaining your answer.

©Teacher Created Materials, Inc.   69   #3302 Daily Skills Practice—Grades 4–5

© Teacher Created Materials, Inc.   217   #3302 Daily Skills Practice—Grades 4–5

Page 70

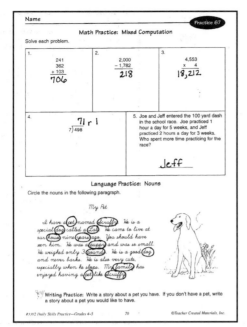

Practice 67

Math Practice: Mixed Computation

Solve each problem.

1.	2.	3.
241 362 + 103 **706**	2,000 − 1,782 **218**	4,553 x 4 **18,212**

4.	5.
7) 498 **71 r 1**	Joe and Jeff entered the 100 yard dash in the school race. Joe practiced 1 hour a day for 5 weeks, and Jeff practiced 2 hours a day for 3 weeks. Who spent more time practicing for the race? **Jeff**

Language Practice: Nouns

Circle the nouns in the following paragraph.

My Pet

I have a pet named Scruffy. He is a special dog called a Lab. He came to live at our house nine years ago. You should have seen him. He was a puppy and was so small. He weighed only 3 pounds. He is a good dog and never barks. He is also very cute, especially when he sleeps. My family has enjoyed having a pet like Scruffy.

✏️ **Writing Practice:** Write a story about a pet you have. If you don't have a pet, write a story about a pet you would like to have.

#3302 Daily Skills Practice—Grades 4–5   70   ©Teacher Created Materials, Inc.

Page 71

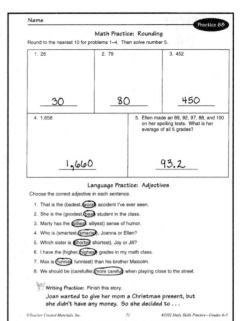

Practice 68

Math Practice: Rounding

Round to the nearest 10 for problems 1–4. Then solve number 5.

1. 26	2. 79	3. 452
30	**80**	**450**

4. 1,658	5. Ellen made an 89, 92, 97, 88, and 100 on her spelling tests. What is her average of all 5 grades?
1,660	**93.2**

Language Practice: Adjectives

Choose the correct adjective in each sentence.

1. That is the (badest, **worst**) accident I've ever seen.
2. She is the (goodest, **best**) student in the class.
3. Marty has the (**silliest**, sillyest) sense of humor.
4. Who is (smartest, **smarter**), Joanna or Ellen?
5. Which sister is (**shorter**, shortest), Joy or Jill?
6. I have the (higher, **highest**) grades in my math class.
7. Max is (**funnier**, funniest) than his brother Malcolm.
8. We should be (carefuller, **more careful**) when playing close to the street.

✏️ **Writing Practice:** Finish this story.
Joan wanted to give her mom a Christmas present, but she didn't have any money. So she decided to . . .

©Teacher Created Materials, Inc.   71   #3302 Daily Skills Practice—Grades 4–5

Page 72

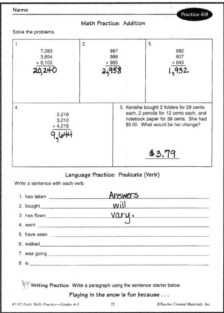

Practice 69

Math Practice: Addition

Solve the problems.

1.	2.	3.
7,283 3,854 + 9,103 **20,240**	987 986 + 985 **2,958**	682 607 + 643 **1,932**

4.	5.
2,218 3,210 + 4,216 **9,644**	Kenisha bought 2 folders for 29 cents each, 2 pencils for 12 cents each, and notebook paper for 39 cents. She had $5.00. What would be her change? **$3.79**

Language Practice: Predicate (Verb)

Write a sentence with each verb.

1. has taken   **Answers**
2. bought   **will**
3. has flown   **vary.**
4. went
5. have seen
6. walked
7. was going
8. is

✏️ **Writing Practice:** Write a paragraph using the sentence starter below.
Playing in the snow is fun because . . .

#3302 Daily Skills Practice—Grades 4–5   72   ©Teacher Created Materials, Inc.

Page 73

Practice 70

Math Practice: Number Order

Write in order from least to greatest for problems 1–4. Then solve problem 5.

1. 13,765 13,705 13,775 13,567	2. 206 260 252 210	3. 6,566 6,565 6,656 6,660
13,567 13,705 **13,765 13,775**	**206 210** **252 260**	**6,565 6,566** **6,656 6,660**

4. 1,042 1,240 1,402 1,024	5. Margaret played basketball for the school's team. During the first six games, she scored 11 points, 8 points, 24 points, 16 points, 9 points, and 15 points. How many points did she score in all six games?
1,024 1,042 **1,240 1,402**	**83 points**

Language Practice: Predicate (Verb)

Write the tenses of the following verbs:

	Past	Past Participle
Example: write	wrote	written
1. sing	**sang**	**sung**
2. go	**went**	**gone**
3. blow	**blew**	**blown**
4. give	**gave**	**given**
5. do	**did**	**done**

✏️ **Writing Practice:** Now choose one verb above and write a paragraph with all three tenses of the verb.

©Teacher Created Materials, Inc.   73   #3302 Daily Skills Practice—Grades 4–5

Page 74

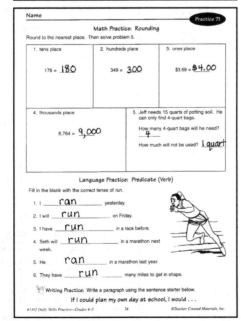

Practice 71

Math Practice: Rounding

Round to the nearest place. Then solve problem 5.

1. tens place	2. hundreds place	3. ones place
176 = **180**	349 = **300**	$3.69 = **$4.00**

4. thousands place	5. Jeff needs 15 quarts of potting soil. He can only find 4-quart bags.
8,764 = **9,000**	How many 4-quart bags will he need? **4** How much will not be used? **1 quart**

Language Practice: Predicate (Verb)

Fill in the blank with the correct tense of *run*.

1. I **ran** yesterday.
2. I will **run** on Friday.
3. I have **run** in a race before.
4. Seth will **run** in a marathon next week.
5. He **ran** in a marathon last year.
6. They have **run** many miles to get in shape.

✏️ **Writing Practice:** Write a paragraph using the sentence starter below.
If I could plan my own day at school, I would . . .

#3302 Daily Skills Practice—Grades 4–5   74   ©Teacher Created Materials, Inc.

Page 75

Practice 72

Math Practice: Decimals

Write a decimal for problems 1–4. Then solve problem 5.

1. $\frac{9}{100}$	2. forty-eight and seven hundredths	3. $2\frac{7}{10}$
.09	**48.07**	**2.7**

4. nine and three tenths	5. If you could only buy one shirt, and the price was 2 for $12.50, how much would one shirt be?
9.3	**$6.25**

Language Practice: Pronouns

Choose a pronoun from the box to take the place of the underlined noun. Write the pronoun on the line after the sentence. Capitalize when necessary.

we   it   they   he   their   she   him   her   our

1. Mr. Griffin is our band teacher. **He**
2. Paul and I play the trumpet. **We**
3. Everyone likes Mr. Griffin because he is a good teacher. **him**
4. Mr. Griffin says that all students need to practice every day. **they**
5. Megan plays the flute. **She**
6. Megan thinks Megan's playing has improved. **her**
7. Mr. Griffin hopes the students' chance of winning the competition will be good. **our or their**

✏️ **Writing Practice:** Parades are always fun to watch. Write a story about watching a parade. Be sure to include all the things you see and hear.

©Teacher Created Materials, Inc.   75   #3302 Daily Skills Practice—Grades 4–5

Page 76

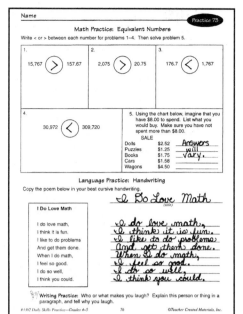

Name _____

Math Practice: Equivalent Numbers

Write < or > between each number for problems 1–4. Then solve problem 5.

1. 15,767 ⟩ 157.67
2. 2,075 ⟩ 20.75
3. 176.7 ⟨ 1,767
4. 30,972 ⟨ 309,720

5. Using the chart below, imagine that you have $8.00 to spend. List what you would buy. Make sure you have not spent more than $8.00.

SALE
Dolls $2.52
Puzzles $1.25
Books $1.75
Cars $1.58
Wagons $4.50

Answers will vary.

Language Practice: Handwriting

Copy the poem below in your best cursive handwriting.

I Do Love Math

I do love math,
I think it is fun.
I like to do problems
And get them done.
When I do math,
I feel so good.
I do so well,
I think you could.

I Do Love Math (title)

I do love math,
I think it is fun.
I like to do problems
And get them done.
When I do math,
I feel so good.
I do so well,
I think you could.

Writing Practice: Who or what makes you laugh? Explain this person or thing in a paragraph, and tell why you laugh.

#3302 Daily Skills Practice—Grades 4–5   76   ©Teacher Created Materials, Inc.

Page 77

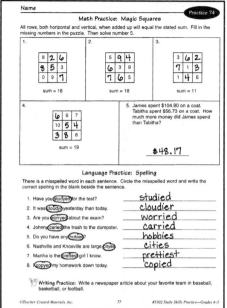

Name _____

Math Practice: Magic Squares

All rows, both horizontal and vertical, when added up will equal the stated sum. Fill in the missing numbers in the puzzle. Then solve number 5.

1.
8	2	6
3	5	3
0	9	7
sum = 16

2.
5	9	4
6	3	9
7	6	5
sum = 18

3.
3	6	2
7	1	3
1	4	6
sum = 11

4.
6	6	7
10	5	4
3	8	8
sum = 19

5. James spent $104.90 on a coat. Tabitha spent $56.73 on a coat. How much more money did James spend than Tabitha?

$48.17

Language Practice: Spelling

There is a misspelled word in each sentence. Circle the misspelled word and write the correct spelling in the blank beside the sentence.

1. Have you studyed for the test?   studied
2. It was cloudyer yesterday than today.   cloudier
3. Are you worryed about the exam?   worried
4. Johnny carried the trash to the dumpster.   carried
5. Do you have any hobbies?   hobbies
6. Nashville and Knoxville are large cityes.   cities
7. Martha is the prettiest girl I know.   prettiest
8. I copyed my homework down today.   copied

Writing Practice: Write a newspaper article about your favorite team in baseball, basketball, or football.

©Teacher Created Materials, Inc.   77   #3302 Daily Skills Practice—Grades 4–5

Page 78

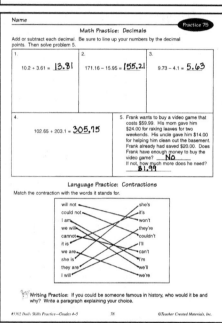

Name _____

Math Practice: Decimals

Add or subtract each decimal. Be sure to line up your numbers by the decimal points. Then solve problem 5.

1. 10.2 + 3.61 = 13.81
2. 171.16 − 15.95 = 155.21
3. 9.73 − 4.1 = 5.63
4. 102.65 + 203.1 = 305.75

5. Frank wants to buy a video game that costs $59.99. His mom gave him $24.00 for raking leaves for two weekends. His uncle gave him $14.00 for helping him clean out the basement. Frank already had saved $20.00. Does Frank have enough money to buy the video game?   NO

If not, how much more does he need? $1.99

Language Practice: Contractions

Match the contraction with the words it stands for.

will not — won't
could not — couldn't
I am — I'm
we will — we'll
cannot — can't
it is — it's
we are — we're
she is — she's
they are — they're
I will — I'll

Writing Practice: If you could be someone famous in history, who would it be and why? Write a paragraph explaining your choice.

#3302 Daily Skills Practice—Grades 4–5   78   ©Teacher Created Materials, Inc.

Page 79

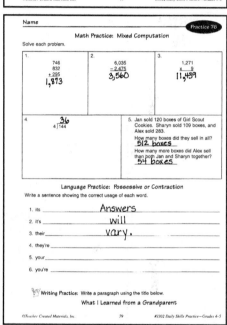

Name _____

Math Practice: Mixed Computation

Solve each problem.

1.
```
  746
  832
+ 295
1,873
```

2.
```
 6,035
−2,475
 3,560
```

3.
```
 1,271
 x    9
11,439
```

4.
```
   36
4)144
```

5. Jan sold 120 boxes of Girl Scout Cookies. Sharyn sold 109 boxes, and Alex sold 283.
How many boxes did they sell in all?   512 boxes
How many more boxes did Alex sell than both Jan and Sharyn together?   54 boxes

Language Practice: Possessive or Contraction

Write a sentence showing the correct usage of each word.

1. its _____   Answers
2. it's _____   will
3. their _____   vary.
4. they're _____
5. your _____
6. you're _____

Writing Practice: Write a paragraph using the title below.

What I Learned from a Grandparent

©Teacher Created Materials, Inc.   79   #3302 Daily Skills Practice—Grades 4–5

Page 80

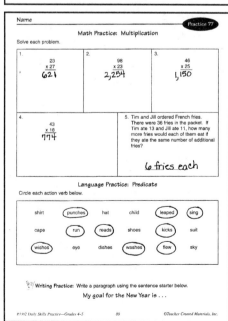

Name _____

Math Practice: Multiplication

Solve each problem.

1.
```
  23
x 27
 621
```

2.
```
   98
 x 23
2,254
```

3.
```
   46
 x 25
1,150
```

4.
```
  43
x 18
 774
```

5. Tim and Jill ordered French fries. There were 36 fries in the packet. If Tim ate 13 and Jill ate 11, how many more fries would each of them eat if they ate the same number of additional fries?

6 fries each

Language Practice: Predicate

Circle each action verb below.

shirt	punches	hat	child	leaped	sing
cape	run	reads	shoes	kicks	suit
wishes	eye	dishes	washes	flew	sky

Writing Practice: Write a paragraph using the sentence starter below.

My goal for the New Year is . . .

#3302 Daily Skills Practice—Grades 4–5   80   ©Teacher Created Materials, Inc.

Page 81

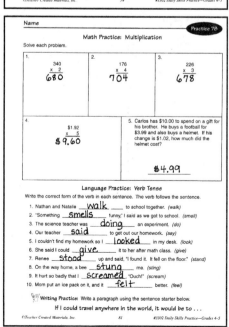

Name _____

Math Practice: Multiplication

Solve each problem.

1.
```
 340
 x  2
 680
```

2.
```
 176
 x  4
 704
```

3.
```
 226
 x  3
 678
```

4.
```
$1.92
 x  5
$9.60
```

5. Carlos has $10.00 to spend on a gift for his brother. He buys a football for $3.99 and also buys a helmet. If his change is $1.02, how much did the helmet cost?

$4.99

Language Practice: Verb Tense

Write the correct form of the verb in each sentence. The verb follows the sentence.

1. Nathan and Natalie _walk_ to school together. *(walk)*
2. "Something _smells_ funny," I said as we got to school. *(smell)*
3. The science teacher was _doing_ an experiment. *(do)*
4. Our teacher _said_ to get out our homework. *(say)*
5. I couldn't find my homework so I _looked_ in my desk. *(look)*
6. She said I could _give_ it to her after math class. *(give)*
7. Renee _stood_ up and said, "I found it. It fell on the floor." *(stand)*
8. On the way home, a bee _stung_ me. *(sting)*
9. It hurt so badly that I _screamed_ "Ouch!" *(scream)*
10. Mom put an ice pack on it, and it _felt_ better. *(feel)*

Writing Practice: Write a paragraph using the sentence starter below.

If I could travel anywhere in the world, it would be to . . .

©Teacher Created Materials, Inc.   81   #3302 Daily Skills Practice—Grades 4–5

Page 82

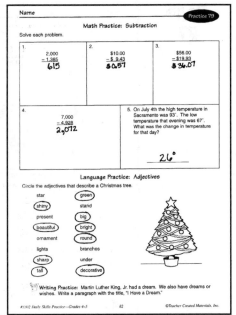

Math Practice: Subtraction

Solve each problem.

1.
2,000
− 1,385
615

2.
$10.00
− $ 9.43
$0.57

3.
$56.00
− $19.93
$36.07

4.
7,000
− 4,928
2,072

5. On July 4th the high temperature in Sacramento was 93°. The low temperature that evening was 67°. What was the change in temperature for that day?

26°

Language Practice: Adjectives

Circle the adjectives that describe a Christmas tree.

star · (shiny) · present · (beautiful) · ornament · lights · (sharp) · (tall) — (green) · stand · (big) · (bright) · (round) · branches · under · (decorative)

Writing Practice: Martin Luther King, Jr. had a dream. We also have dreams or wishes. Write a paragraph with the title, "I Have a Dream."

#3302 Daily Skills Practice—Grades 4–5 · 82 · ©Teacher Created Materials, Inc.

Page 83

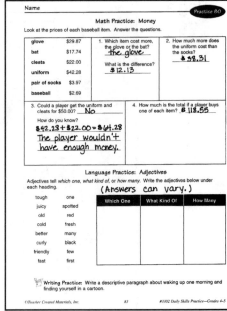

Math Practice: Money

Look at the prices of each baseball item. Answer the questions.

glove	$29.87
bat	$17.74
cleats	$22.00
uniform	$42.28
pair of socks	$3.97
baseball	$2.69

1. Which item cost more, the glove or the bat? the glove
What is the difference? $12.13

2. How much more does the uniform cost than the socks? $38.31

3. Could a player get the uniform and cleats for $50.00? No
How do you know? $42.28 + $22.00 = $64.28 The player wouldn't have enough money.

4. How much is the total if a player buys one of each item? $118.55

Language Practice: Adjectives

Adjectives tell which one, what kind of, or how many. Write the adjectives below under each heading. (Answers can vary.)

tough · one · juicy · spotted · old · red · cold · fresh · better · many · curly · black · friendly · few · fast · first

Which One	What Kind Of	How Many

Writing Practice: Write a descriptive paragraph about waking up one morning and finding yourself in a cartoon.

©Teacher Created Materials, Inc. · 83 · #3302 Daily Skills Practice—Grades 4–5

Page 84

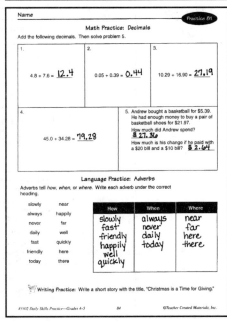

Math Practice: Decimals

Add the following decimals. Then solve problem 5.

1. 4.8 + 7.6 = 12.4

2. 0.05 + 0.39 = 0.44

3. 10.29 + 16.90 = 27.19

4. 45.0 + 34.28 = 79.28

5. Andrew bought a basketball for $5.39. He had enough money to buy a pair of basketball shoes for $21.97. How much did Andrew spend? $27.36
How much is his change if he paid with a $20 bill and a $10 bill? $2.64

Language Practice: Adverbs

Adverbs tell how, when, or where. Write each adverb under the correct heading.

slowly · always · never · daily · fast · friendly · today — near · happily · far · well · quickly · here · there

How	When	Where
slowly fast friendly happily well quickly	always never daily today	near far here there

Writing Practice: Write a short story with the title, "Christmas is a Time for Giving."

#3302 Daily Skills Practice—Grades 4–5 · 84 · ©Teacher Created Materials, Inc.

Page 85

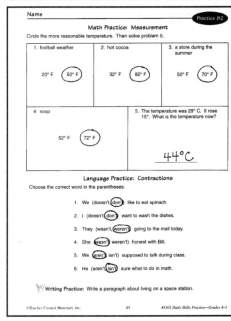

Math Practice: Measurement

Circle the more reasonable temperature. Then solve problem 5.

1. football weather — 20° F · (50° F)

2. hot cocoa — 32° F · (82° F)

3. a store during the summer — 50° F · (70° F)

4. soup — 52° F · (72° F)

5. The temperature was 29° C. It rose 15°. What is the temperature now?

44° C

Language Practice: Contractions

Choose the correct word in the parentheses.

1. We (doesn't, (don't)) like to eat spinach.
2. I (doesn't, (don't)) want to wash the dishes.
3. They (wasn't, (weren't)) going to the mall today.
4. She ((wasn't), weren't) honest with Bill.
5. We ((aren't), isn't) supposed to talk during class.
6. He (aren't, (isn't)) sure what to do in math.

Writing Practice: Write a paragraph about living on a space station.

©Teacher Created Materials, Inc. · 85 · #3302 Daily Skills Practice—Grades 4–5

Page 86

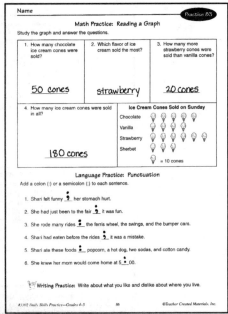

Math Practice: Reading a Graph

Study the graph and answer the questions.

1. How many chocolate ice cream cones were sold? 50 cones

2. Which flavor of ice cream sold the most? strawberry

3. How many more strawberry cones were sold than vanilla cones? 20 cones

4. How many ice cream cones were sold in all? 180 cones

Ice Cream Cones Sold on Sunday

Chocolate · Vanilla · Strawberry · Sherbet

= 10 cones

Language Practice: Punctuation

Add a colon (:) or a semicolon (;) to each sentence.

1. Shari felt funny ; her stomach hurt.
2. She had just been to the fair ; it was fun.
3. She rode many rides : the ferris wheel, the swings, and the bumper cars.
4. Shari had eaten before the rides ; it was a mistake.
5. Shari ate these foods : popcorn, a hot dog, two sodas, and cotton candy.
6. She knew her mom would come home at 5 : 00.

Writing Practice: Write about what you like and dislike about where you live.

#3302 Daily Skills Practice—Grades 4–5 · 86 · ©Teacher Created Materials, Inc.

Page 87

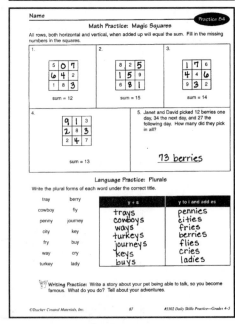

Math Practice: Magic Squares

All rows, both horizontal and vertical, when added up will equal the sum. Fill in the missing numbers in the squares.

1.
5	0	7
6	4	2
1	8	3
sum = 12

2.
8	2	5
1	5	9
6	8	1
sum = 15

3.
1	7	6
4	4	6
9	3	2
sum = 14

4.
9	1	3
2	8	3
2	4	7
sum = 13

5. Janet and David picked 12 berries one day, 34 the next day, and 27 the following day. How many did they pick in all?

73 berries

Language Practice: Plurals

Write the plural forms of each word under the correct title.

tray · cowboy · penny · city · fry · way · turkey — berry · fly · journey · key · buy · cry · lady

y + s	y to i and add es
trays cowboys ways turkeys journeys keys buys	pennies cities fries berries flies cries ladies

Writing Practice: Write a story about your pet being able to talk, so you become famous. What do you do? Tell about your adventures.

©Teacher Created Materials, Inc. · 87 · #3302 Daily Skills Practice—Grades 4–5

Page 88

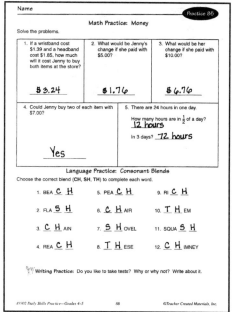

Page 89

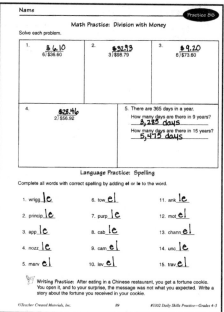

Page 90

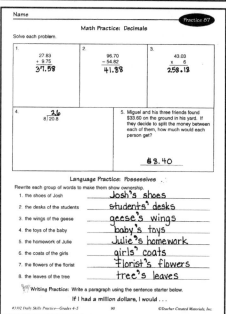

Page 91

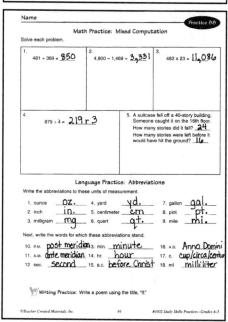

Page 92

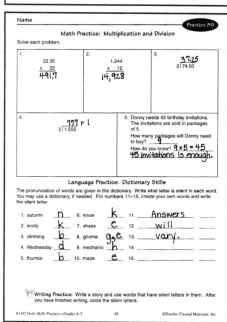

Page 93

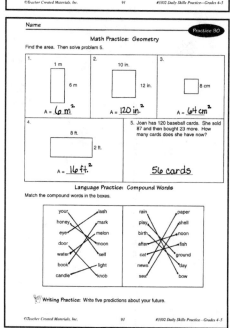

Page 94

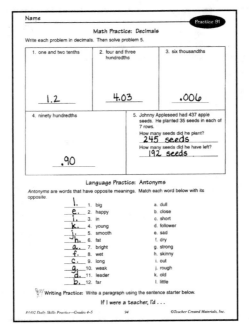

Page 94 content:

Name _____ Practice 91

Math Practice: Decimals

Write each problem in decimals. Then solve problem 5.

1. one and two tenths	2. four and three hundredths	3. six thousandths
1.2	4.03	.006

4. ninety hundredths	5. Johnny Appleseed had 437 apple seeds. He planted 35 seeds in each of 7 rows. How many seeds did he plant? 245 seeds How many seeds did he have left? 192 seeds
.90	

Language Practice: Antonyms

Antonyms are words that have opposite meanings. Match each word below with its opposite.

l. 1. big	a. dull
e. 2. happy	b. close
i. 3. in	c. short
k. 4. young	d. follower
j. 5. smooth	e. sad
h. 6. fat	f. dry
a. 7. bright	g. strong
f. 8. wet	h. skinny
c. 9. long	i. out
g. 10. weak	j. rough
d. 11. leader	k. old
b. 12. far	l. little

Writing Practice: Write a paragraph using the sentence starter below.

If I were a teacher, I'd . . .

#3302 Daily Skills Practice—Grades 4–5   94   ©Teacher Created Materials, Inc.

Page 95

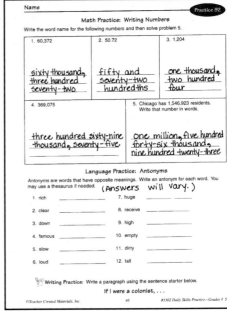

Name _____ Practice 92

Math Practice: Writing Numbers

Write the word name for the following numbers and then solve problem 5.

1. 60,372	2. 50.72	3. 1,204
sixty thousand, three hundred seventy-two	fifty and seventy-two hundredths	one thousand, two hundred four

4. 369,075	5. Chicago has 1,546,923 residents. Write that number in words.
three hundred sixty-nine thousand, seventy-five	one million, five hundred forty-six thousand, nine hundred twenty-three

Language Practice: Antonyms

Antonyms are words that have opposite meanings. Write an antonym for each word. You may use a thesaurus if needed. (Answers will vary.)

1. rich _____	7. huge _____
2. clear _____	8. receive _____
3. down _____	9. high _____
4. famous _____	10. empty _____
5. slow _____	11. dirty _____
6. loud _____	12. tall _____

Writing Practice: Write a paragraph using the sentence starter below.

If I were a colonist, . . .

©Teacher Created Materials, Inc.   95   #3302 Daily Skills Practice—Grades 4–5

Page 96

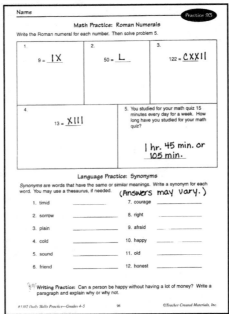

Name _____ Practice 93

Math Practice: Roman Numerals

Write the Roman numeral for each number. Then solve problem 5.

1. 9 = IX	2. 50 = L	3. 122 = CXXII

4. 13 = XIII	5. You studied for your math quiz 15 minutes every day for a week. How long have you studied for your math quiz? 1 hr. 45 min. or 105 min.

Language Practice: Synonyms

Synonyms are words that have the same or similar meanings. Write a synonym for each word. You may use a thesaurus, if needed. (Answers may vary.)

1. timid _____	7. courage _____
2. sorrow _____	8. right _____
3. plain _____	9. afraid _____
4. cold _____	10. happy _____
5. sound _____	11. old _____
6. friend _____	12. honest _____

Writing Practice: Can a person be happy without having a lot of money? Write a paragraph and explain why or why not.

#3302 Daily Skills Practice—Grades 4–5   96   ©Teacher Created Materials, Inc.

Page 97

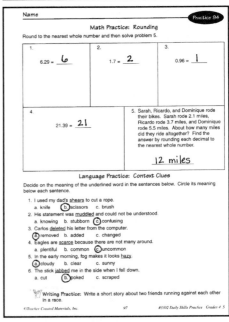

Name _____ Practice 94

Math Practice: Rounding

Round to the nearest whole number and then solve problem 5.

1. 6.29 = 6	2. 1.7 = 2	3. 0.96 = 1

4. 21.39 = 21	5. Sarah, Ricardo, and Dominique rode their bikes. Sarah rode 2.1 miles, Ricardo rode 3.7 miles, and Dominique rode 5.5 miles. About how many miles did they ride altogether? Find the answer by rounding each decimal to the nearest whole number. 12 miles

Language Practice: Context Clues

Decide on the meaning of the underlined word in the sentences below. Circle its meaning below each sentence.

1. I used my dad's <u>shears</u> to cut a rope.
   a. knife   (b.)scissors   c. brush
2. His statement was <u>muddled</u> and could not be understood.
   a. knowing   b. stubborn   (c.)confusing
3. Carlos <u>deleted</u> his letter from the computer.
   (a.)removed   b. added   c. changed
4. Eagles are <u>scarce</u> because there are not many around.
   a. plentiful   b. common   (c.)uncommon
5. In the early morning, fog makes it looks <u>hazy</u>.
   (a.)cloudy   b. clear   c. sunny
6. The stick <u>jabbed</u> me in the side when I fell down.
   a. cut   (b.)poked   c. scraped

Writing Practice: Write a short story about two friends running against each other in a race.

©Teacher Created Materials, Inc.   97   #3302 Daily Skills Practice—Grades 4–5

Page 98

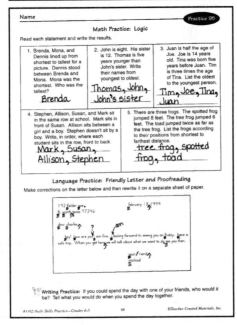

Name _____ Practice 95

Math Practice: Logic

Read each statement and write the results.

1. Brenda, Mona, and Dennis lined up from shortest to tallest for a picture. Dennis stood between Brenda and Mona. Mona was the shortest. Who was the tallest? Brenda	2. John is eight. His sister is 12. Thomas is five years younger than John's sister. Write their names from youngest to oldest. Thomas, John, John's sister	3. Juan is half the age of Joe. Joe is 14 years old. Tina was born five years before Juan. Tim is three times the age of Tina. List the oldest to the youngest person. Tim, Joe, Tina, Juan
4. Stephen, Allison, Susan, and Mark sit in the same row at school. Mark sits in front of Susan. Allison sits between a girl and a boy. Stephen doesn't sit by a boy. Write, in order, where each student sits in the row, front to back. Mark, Susan, Allison, Stephen	5. There are three frogs. The spotted frog jumped 8 feet. The tree frog jumped 6 feet. The toad jumped twice as far as the tree frog. List the frogs according to their positions from shortest to farthest distance. tree frog, spotted frog, toad	

Language Practice: Friendly Letter and Proofreading

Make corrections on the letter below and then rewrite it on a separate sheet of paper.

Writing Practice: If you could spend the day with one of your friends, who would it be? Tell what you would do when you spend the day together.

#3302 Daily Skills Practice—Grades 4–5   98   ©Teacher Created Materials, Inc.

Page 99

Name _____ Practice 96

Math Practice: Estimation and Decimals

Estimate to the nearest tenth. Then solve problem 5.

1. 5.67 = 5.7	2. 71.26 = 71.3	3. 64.74 = 64.7

4. 9,317.72 = 9,317.7	5. Jennifer and Marsha sold $75.63 worth of cookies. Their goal was to sell $100.00 worth. How much more would they have to sell in order to reach their goal? $24.37

Language Practice: Sequencing

Number the events in time order.

1. Going to the movies
   5 We watched the movie that started at 7:00 P.M.
   4 Jake bought popcorn before the movie started; it was delicious.
   2 We stood in line 20 minutes for tickets.
   6 We went to eat at 9:00 P.M.
   3 We each bought our own tickets.
   1 Jake and Billy decided to go to the movies.

2. Morning routine
   2 I get dressed.
   1 I get up at 6:30 A.M.
   6 My mom drives me to school.
   5 Our family eats breakfast together.
   3 Mom blows the horn, because I am running late.
   4 I brush my teeth.

3. Writing a letter
   3 Jo sealed the envelope.
   1 I gave Jo a piece of paper to write a letter.
   5 She asked me to mail the letter for her.
   4 Jo put the stamp on the letter.
   2 She wrote a letter to her grandmother.
   6 Jo waited for an answer to her letter.

4. Making cookies
   5 I put the cookies in the oven.
   3 I mixed the flour, sugar, and eggs.
   4 I measured the flour, sugar, and eggs.
   1 I placed the ingredients on the sink.
   2 I warmed up the oven.
   6 I let the cookies cool so I could eat them.

Writing Practice: Write a paragraph about your evening routine each night. Make sure all sentences are in correct sentence order.

©Teacher Created Materials, Inc.   99   #3302 Daily Skills Practice—Grades 4–5

Page numbers (left margin labels): Page 94, Page 95, Page 96, Page 97, Page 98, Page 99

Page 100

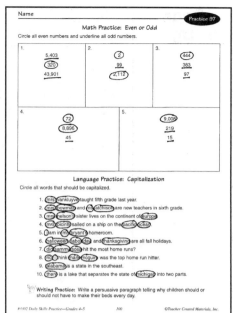

Math Practice: Even or Odd
Circle all even numbers and underline all odd numbers.

| 1. 5,403 / 320 / 43,901 | 2. 2 / 99 / 2,112 | 3. 444 / 383 / 97 |
| 4. 72 / 8,896 / 45 | 5. 9,008 / 219 / 15 | |

Language Practice: Capitalization
Circle all words that should be capitalized.

1. mrs. frankluyve taught fifth grade last year.
2. mrs. bowman and ms. atchison are new teachers in sixth grade.
3. mrs. nelson's sister lives on the continent of europe.
4. mrs. picirilli sailed on a ship on the pacific ocean.
5. i am in mr. bryant's homeroom.
6. halloween, labor day, and thanksgiving are all fall holidays.
7. did sammy sosa hit the most home runs?
8. i don't think mark moguir was the top home run hitter.
9. alabama is a state in the southeast.
10. there is a lake that separates the state of michigan into two parts.

Writing Practice: Write a persuasive paragraph telling why children should or should not have to make their beds every day.

#3302 Daily Skills Practice—Grades 4–5   100   ©Teacher Created Materials, Inc.

Page 101

Math Practice: Money
Write what type of bills and coins equal each money value.

1. $17.53	2. $107.65	3. $75.25
Answers will vary.	Answers will vary.	Answers will vary.
4. $63.71	5. Erica bought cereal for $2.39, juice for $1.59, and flour for $1.25. How much did she spend?
Answers will vary.	$5.23

Language Practice: Prefix/Suffix
Add a *prefix* to each word and then write a sentence with each word.

1. ___ clear   Answers
2. ___ do   will
3. ___ order   vary.
4. ___ trust

Add a *suffix* to each word and then write a sentence with each word.

5. care ___   Answers
6. kind ___   will
7. sail ___   vary.
8. help ___

Writing Practice: You are sleeping soundly when the phone rings and wakes you up. Write a story about what happens.

©Teacher Created Materials, Inc.   101   #3302 Daily Skills Practice—Grades 4–5

Page 102

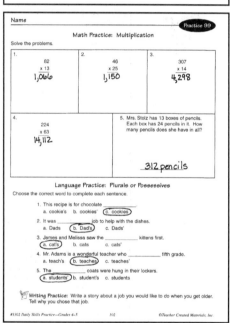

Math Practice: Multiplication
Solve the problems.

| 1. 82 × 13 = 1,066 | 2. 46 × 25 = 1,150 | 3. 307 × 14 = 4,298 |
| 4. 224 × 63 = 14,112 | 5. Mrs. Stolz has 13 boxes of pencils. Each box has 24 pencils in it. How many pencils does she have in all? 312 pencils |

Language Practice: Plurals or Possessives
Choose the correct word to complete each sentence.

1. This recipe is for chocolate _____
   a. cookie's   b. cookies'   **c. cookies**
2. It was _____ job to help with the dishes.
   a. Dads   **b. Dad's**   c. Dads'
3. James and Melissa saw the _____ kittens first.
   a. cat's   b. cats   c. cats'
4. Mr. Adams is a wonderful teacher who _____ fifth grade.
   a. teach's   **b. teaches**   c. teaches'
5. The _____ coats were hung in their lockers.
   a. students'   b. student's   c. students

Writing Practice: Write a story about a job you would like to do when you get older. Tell why you chose that job.

#3302 Daily Skills Practice—Grades 4–5   102   ©Teacher Created Materials, Inc.

Page 103

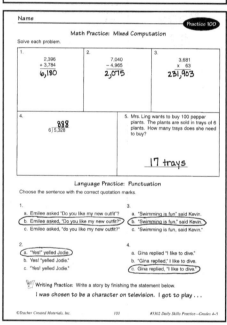

Math Practice: Mixed Computation
Solve each problem.

| 1. 2,396 + 3,784 = 6,180 | 2. 7,040 − 4,965 = 2,075 | 3. 3,681 × 63 = 231,903 |
| 4. 6)5,328 = 888 | 5. Mrs. Ling wants to buy 100 pepper plants. The plants are sold in trays of 6 plants. How many trays does she need to buy? 17 trays |

Language Practice: Punctuation
Choose the sentence with the correct quotation marks.

1.
   a. Emilee asked "Do you like my new outfit"?
   b. Emilee asked, "Do you like my new outfit?"
   c. Emilee asked, "do you like my new outfit?"

2.
   a. "Yes!" yelled Jodie.
   b. Yes! "yelled Jodie."
   c. "Yes! yelled Jodie."

3.
   a. "Swimming is fun" said Kevin.
   b. "Swimming is fun," said Kevin.
   c. "Swimming is fun, said Kevin."

4.
   a. Gina replied "I like to dive."
   b. "Gina replied," I like to dive.
   c. Gina replied, "I like to dive."

Writing Practice: Write a story by finishing the statement below.
I was chosen to be a character on television. I got to play . . .

©Teacher Created Materials, Inc.   103   #3302 Daily Skills Practice—Grades 4–5

Page 104

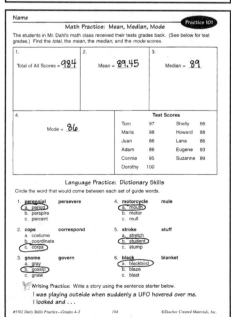

Math Practice: Mean, Median, Mode
The students in Mr. Dahl's math class received their tests grades back. (See below for test grades.) Find the *total*, the *mean*, the *median*, and the *mode* scores.

| 1. Total of All Scores = 984 | 2. Mean = 89.45 | 3. Median = 89 |
| 4. Mode = 86 | **Test Scores** |

Test Scores:
Tom 97, Shelly 66
Maria 98, Howard 88
Juan 86, Lana 86
Adam 86, Eugene 93
Connie 95, Suzanne 89
Dorothy 100

Language Practice: Dictionary Skills
Circle the word that would come between each set of guide words.

1. perennial _____ persevere   4. motorcycle _____ mule
   a. period   **a. mouth**
   b. perspire   b. motor
   c. percent   c. mull

2. cope _____ correspond   5. stroke _____ stuff
   a. costume   a. stretch
   b. coordinate   **b. student**
   c. corps   c. stump

3. gnome _____ govern   6. black _____ blanket
   a. gray   **a. blackbird**
   b. gossip   b. blaze
   c. gnaw   c. blast

Writing Practice: Write a story using the sentence starter below.
I was playing outside when suddenly a UFO hovered over me. I looked and . . .

#3302 Daily Skills Practice—Grades 4–5   104   ©Teacher Created Materials, Inc.

Page 105

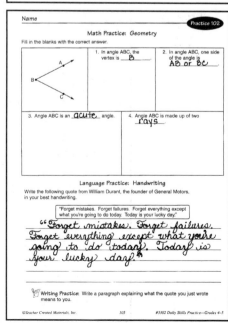

Math Practice: Geometry
Fill in the blanks with the correct answer.

| 1. In angle ABC, the vertex is B. | 2. In angle ABC, one side of the angle is AB or BC. |
| 3. Angle ABC is an acute angle. | 4. Angle ABC is made up of two rays. |

Language Practice: Handwriting
Write the following quote from William Durant, the founder of General Motors, in your best handwriting.

"Forget mistakes. Forget failures. Forget everything except what you're going to do today. Today is your lucky day."

"Forget mistakes. Forget failures. Forget everything except what you're going to do today. Today is your lucky day."

Writing Practice: Write a paragraph explaining what the quote you just wrote means to you.

©Teacher Created Materials, Inc.   105   #3302 Daily Skills Practice—Grades 4–5

Page 106

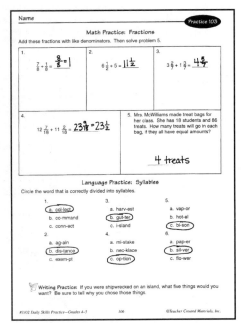

Practice 103

Math Practice: Fractions

Add these fractions with like denominators. Then solve problem 5.

1. $\frac{7}{8} + \frac{1}{8} = \frac{8}{8} = 1$

2. $6\frac{1}{2} + 5 = 11\frac{1}{2}$

3. $3\frac{2}{7} + 1\frac{3}{7} = 4\frac{5}{7}$

4. $12\frac{7}{18} + 11\frac{2}{18} = 23\frac{9}{18} = 23\frac{1}{2}$

5. Mrs. McWilliams made treat bags for her class. She has 18 students and 86 treats. How many treats will go in each bag, if they all have equal amounts?

4 treats

Language Practice: Syllables

Circle the word that is correctly divided into syllables.

1.
a. col-lect (circled)
b. co-mmand
c. conn-ect

2.
a. ag-ain
b. dis-tance (circled)
c. exem-pt

3.
a. harv-est
b. gut-ter (circled)
c. i-sland

4.
a. mi-stake
b. nec-klace
c. op-tion (circled)

5.
a. vap-or
b. hot-el
c. bi-son (circled)

6.
a. pap-er
b. sil-ver (circled)
c. flo-wer

Writing Practice: If you were shipwrecked on an island, what five things would you want? Be sure to tell why you chose those things.

#3302 Daily Skills Practice—Grades 4–5   106   ©Teacher Created Materials, Inc.

Page 107

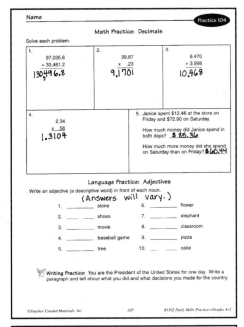

Practice 104

Math Practice: Decimals

Solve each problem.

1.
```
   97,035.6
+  33,446.2
 130,496.8
```

2.
```
   39.87
x    .23
  9.1701
```

3.
```
    6.470
+  3.998
  10.468
```

4.
```
   2.34
x   .56
 1.3104
```

5. Janice spent $12.46 at the store on Friday and $72.90 on Saturday.

How much money did Janice spend in both days? $85.36

How much more money did she spend on Saturday than on Friday? $60.44

Language Practice: Adjectives

Write an adjective (a descriptive word) in front of each noun.

(Answers will vary.)

1. _____ stone
2. _____ shoes
3. _____ movie
4. _____ baseball game
5. _____ tree
6. _____ flower
7. _____ elephant
8. _____ classroom
9. _____ pizza
10. _____ cake

Writing Practice: You are the President of the United States for one day. Write a paragraph and tell about what you did and what decisions you made for the country.

©Teacher Created Materials, Inc.   107   #3302 Daily Skills Practice—Grades 4–5

Page 108

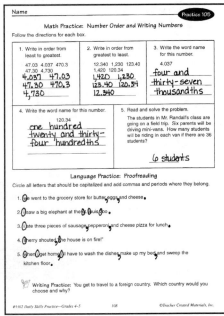

Practice 105

Math Practice: Number Order and Writing Numbers

Follow the directions for each box.

1. Write in order from least to greatest.

47.03 4.037 470.3
47.30 4,730

4.037 47.03
47.30 470.3
4,730

2. Write in order from greatest to least.

12.340 1,230 123.40
1,420 120.34

1,420 1,230
123.40 120.34
12.340

3. Write the word name for this number.

4.037

four and thirty-seven thousandths

4. Write the word name for this number.

120.34

one hundred twenty and thirty-four hundredths

5. Read and solve the problem.

The students in Mr. Randall's class are going on a field trip. Six parents will be driving mini-vans. How many students will be riding in each van if there are 36 students?

6 students

Language Practice: Proofreading

Circle all letters that should be capitalized and add commas and periods where they belong.

1. We went to the grocery store for butter eggs and cheese.

2. I saw a big elephant at the St. Louis Zoo.

3. I ate three pieces of sausage pepperoni and cheese pizza for lunch.

4. Cherry shouted the house is on fire!

5. When I get home I'll have to wash the dishes make up my bed and sweep the kitchen floor.

Writing Practice: You get to travel to a foreign country. Which country would you choose and why?

#3302 Daily Skills Practice—Grades 4–5   108   ©Teacher Created Materials, Inc.

Page 109

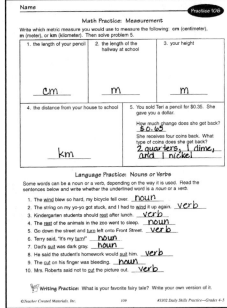

Practice 106

Math Practice: Measurement

Write which metric measure you would use to measure the following: cm (centimeter), m (meter), or km (kilometer). Then solve problem 5.

1. the length of your pencil
cm

2. the length of the hallway at school
m

3. your height
m

4. the distance from your house to school
km

5. You sold Teri a pencil for $0.35. She gave you a dollar.

How much change does she get back? $0.65

She receives four coins back. What type of coins does she get back?
2 quarters, 1 dime, and 1 nickel

Language Practice: Nouns or Verbs

Some words can be a noun or a verb, depending on the way it is used. Read the sentences below and write whether the underlined word is a noun or a verb.

1. The wind blew so hard, my bicycle fell over. noun
2. The string on my yo-yo got stuck, and I had to wind it up again. verb
3. Kindergarten students should rest after lunch. verb
4. The rest of the animals in the zoo went to sleep. noun
5. Go down the street and turn left onto Front Street. verb
6. Terry said, "It's my turn!" noun
7. Dad's suit was dark gray. noun
8. He said the student's homework would suit him. verb
9. The cut on his finger was bleeding. noun
10. Mrs. Roberts said not to cut the picture out. verb

Writing Practice: What is your favorite fairy tale? Write your own version of it.

©Teacher Created Materials, Inc.   109   #3302 Daily Skills Practice—Grades 4–5

Page 110

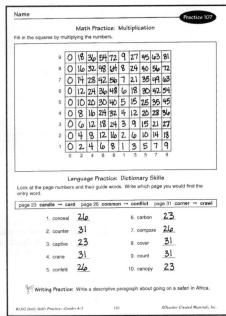

Practice 107

Math Practice: Multiplication

Fill in the squares by multiplying the numbers.

×	0	2	4	6	8	1	3	5	7	9
9	0	18	36	54	72	9	27	45	63	81
8	0	16	32	48	64	8	24	40	56	72
7	0	14	28	42	56	7	21	35	49	63
6	0	12	24	36	48	6	18	30	42	54
5	0	10	20	30	40	5	15	25	35	45
4	0	8	16	24	32	4	12	20	28	36
3	0	6	12	18	24	3	9	15	21	27
2	0	4	8	12	16	2	6	10	14	18
1	0	2	4	6	8	1	3	5	7	9

Language Practice: Dictionary Skills

Look at the page numbers and their guide words. Write which page you would find the entry word.

page 23 candle → card   page 26 common → conflict   page 31 corner → crawl

1. conceal   26
2. counter   31
3. captive   23
4. crane   31
5. confetti 26
6. carbon   23
7. compare   26
8. cover   31
9. count   31
10. canopy   23

Writing Practice: Write a descriptive paragraph about going on a safari in Africa.

#3302 Daily Skills Practice—Grades 4–5   110   ©Teacher Created Materials, Inc.

Page 111

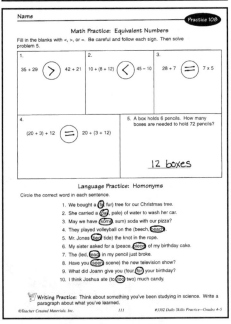

Practice 108

Math Practice: Equivalent Numbers

Fill in the blanks with <, >, or =. Be careful and follow each sign. Then solve problem 5.

1. $35 + 29 \,\,\boxed{>}\,\, 42 + 21$

2. $10 + (8 + 12) \,\,\boxed{<}\,\, 45 - 10$

3. $28 + 7 \,\,\boxed{=}\,\, 7 \times 5$

4. $(20 + 3) + 12 \,\,\boxed{=}\,\, 20 + (3 + 12)$

5. A box holds 6 pencils. How many boxes are needed to hold 72 pencils?

12 boxes

Language Practice: Homonyms

Circle the correct word in each sentence.

1. We bought a (fir, fur) tree for our Christmas tree.
2. She carried a (pail, pale) of water to wash her car.
3. May we have (some, sum) soda with our pizza?
4. They played volleyball on the (beech, beach).
5. Mr. Jones (tied, tide) the knot in the rope.
6. My sister asked for a (peace, piece) of my birthday cake.
7. The (led, lead) in my pencil just broke.
8. Have you (seen, scene) the new television show?
9. What did Joann give you (four, for) your birthday?
10. I think Joshua ate (to, too, two) much candy.

Writing Practice: Think about something you've been studying in science. Write a paragraph about what you've learned.

©Teacher Created Materials, Inc.   111   #3302 Daily Skills Practice—Grades 4–5

Page 112

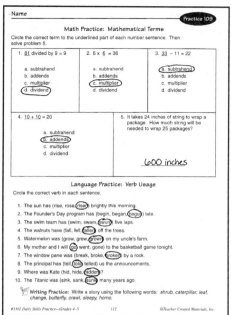

Practice 109

Math Practice: Mathematical Terms

Circle the correct term to the underlined part of each number sentence. Then solve problem 5.

1. <u>81</u> divided by 9 = 9
   a. subtrahend
   b. addends
   c. multiplier
   d. (dividend)

2. 6 x <u>6</u> = 36
   a. subtrahend
   b. addends
   c. (multiplier)
   d. dividend

3. 33 – <u>11</u> = 22
   a. (subtrahend)
   b. addends
   c. multiplier
   d. dividend

4. <u>10 + 10</u> = 20
   a. subtrahend
   b. (addends)
   c. multiplier
   d. dividend

5. It takes 24 inches of string to wrap a package. How much string will be needed to wrap 25 packages?

600 inches

Language Practice: Verb Usage

Circle the correct verb in each sentence.

1. The sun has (rise, rose, (risen)) brightly this morning.
2. The Founder's Day program has (begin, began, (begun)) late.
3. The swim team has (swim, swam, (swum)) five laps.
4. The walnuts have (fall, fell, (fallen)) off the trees.
5. Watermelon was (grow, grew, (grown)) on my uncle's farm.
6. My mother and I will ((go) went, gone) to the basketball game tonight.
7. The window pane was (break, broke, (broken)) by a rock.
8. The principal has (tell, (told) telled) us the announcements.
9. Where was Kate (hid, hide, (hidden))?
10. The *Titanic* was (sink, sank, (sunk)) many years ago.

Writing Practice: Write a story using the following words: *shrub, caterpillar, leaf, change, butterfly, crawl, sleepy, home.*

#3302 Daily Skills Practice—Grades 4–5   112   ©Teacher Created Materials, Inc.

Page 113

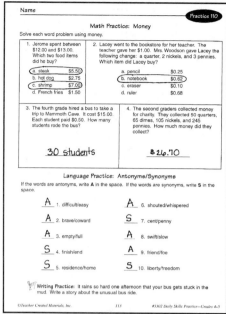

Practice 110

Math Practice: Money

Solve each word problem using money.

1. Jerome spent between $12.00 and $13.00. Which two food items did he buy?
   a. (steak) $5.50
   b. hot dog $2.75
   c. (shrimp) $7.00
   d. French fries $1.50

2. Lacey went to the bookstore for her teacher. The teacher gave her $1.00. Mrs. Woodson gave Lacey the following change: a quarter, 2 nickels, and 3 pennies. Which item did Lacey buy?
   a. pencil $0.25
   b. (notebook) $0.62
   c. eraser $0.10
   d. ruler $0.68

3. The fourth grade hired a bus to take a trip to Mammoth Cave. It cost $15.00. Each student paid $0.50. How many students rode the bus?

30 students

4. The second graders collected money for charity. They collected 50 quarters, 65 dimes, 105 nickels, and 245 pennies. How much money did they collect?

$26.70

Language Practice: Antonyms/Synonyms

If the words are antonyms, write **A** in the space. If the words are synonyms, write **S** in the space.

A 1. difficult/easy
A 2. brave/coward
A 3. empty/full
S 4. finish/end
S 5. residence/home
A 6. shouted/whispered
S 7. cent/penny
A 8. swift/slow
A 9. friend/foe
S 10. liberty/freedom

Writing Practice: It rains so hard one afternoon that your bus gets stuck in the mud. Write a story about the unusual bus ride.

©Teacher Created Materials, Inc.   113   #3302 Daily Skills Practice—Grades 4–5

Page 114

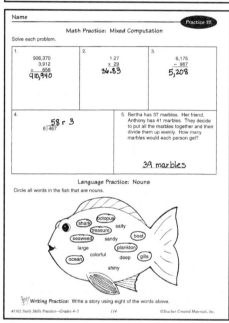

Practice 111

Math Practice: Mixed Computation

Solve each problem.

1.
906,370
3,912
+ 658
910,940

2.
1.27
x 29
36.83

3.
6,175
– 967
5,208

4.
58 r 3
8)467

5. Bertha has 37 marbles. Her friend, Anthony has 41 marbles. They decide to put all the marbles together and then divide them up evenly. How many marbles would each person get?

39 marbles

Language Practice: Nouns

Circle all words in the fish that are nouns.

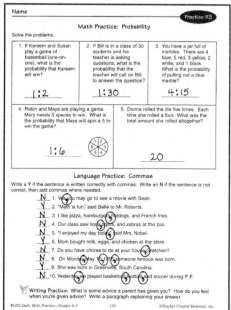

shark, octopus, treasure, seaweed, boat, plankton, gills, ocean — (nouns circled); salty, sandy, large, colorful, deep, shiny

Writing Practice: Write a story using eight of the words above.

#3302 Daily Skills Practice—Grades 4–5   114   ©Teacher Created Materials, Inc.

Page 115

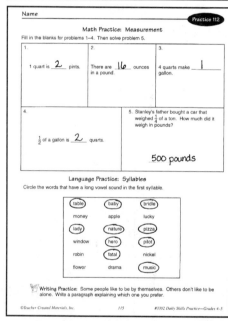

Practice 112

Math Practice: Measurement

Fill in the blanks for problems 1–4. Then solve problem 5.

1. 1 quart is **2** pints.
2. There are **16** ounces in a pound.
3. 4 quarts make **1** gallon.
4. ½ of a gallon is **2** quarts.
5. Stanley's father bought a car that weighed ¼ of a ton. How much did it weigh in pounds?

500 pounds

Language Practice: Syllables

Circle the words that have a long vowel sound in the first syllable.

(table)	(baby)	(bridle)
money	apple	lucky
(lady)	(nature)	(pizza)
window	(hero)	(pilot)
robin	(fatal)	nickel
flower	drama	(music)

Writing Practice: Some people like to be by themselves. Others don't like to be alone. Write a paragraph explaining which one you prefer.

©Teacher Created Materials, Inc.   115   #3302 Daily Skills Practice—Grades 4–5

Page 116

Practice 113

Math Practice: Probability

Solve the problems.

1. If Kareem and Susan play a game of basketball (one-on-one), what is the probability that Kareem will win?

1:2

2. If Bill is in a class of 30 students and his teacher is asking questions, what is the probability that the teacher will call on Bill to answer the question?

1:30

3. You have a jar full of marbles. There are 4 blue, 5 red, 3 yellow, 2 white, and 1 black. What is the probability of pulling out a blue marble?

4:15

4. Robin and Maya are playing a game. Mary needs 5 spaces to win. What is the probability that Maya will spin a 5 to win the game?

1:6

5. Donna rolled the die five times. Each time she rolled a four. What was the total amount she rolled altogether?

20

Language Practice: Commas

Write a Y if the sentence is written correctly with commas. Write an N if the sentence is not correct, then add commas where needed.

N 1. Yes you may go to see a movie with Sean.
Y 2. "Math is fun," said Belle to Mr. Roberts.
N 3. I like pizza, hamburgers, hotdogs, and French fries.
N 4. Our class saw lions, tigers, and zebras at the zoo.
N 5. "I enjoyed my day today," said Mrs. Nobel.
Y 6. Mom bought milk, eggs, and chicken at the store.
N 7. Do you have chores to do at your house, Gretchen?
N 8. On Monday, May 1, 1992, someone famous was born.
Y 9. She was born in Greenville, South Carolina.
N 10. Yesterday we played basketball, football, and soccer during P.E.

Writing Practice: What is some advice a parent has given you? How do you feel when you're given advice? Write a paragraph explaining your answer.

#3302 Daily Skills Practice—Grades 4–5   116   ©Teacher Created Materials, Inc.

Page 117

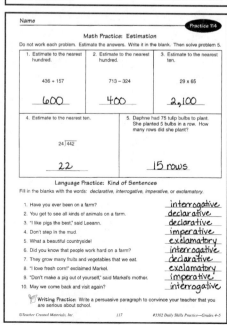

Practice 114

Math Practice: Estimation

Do not work each problem. Estimate the answers. Write it in the blank. Then solve problem 5.

1. Estimate to the nearest hundred.
436 + 157
600

2. Estimate to the nearest hundred.
713 – 324
400

3. Estimate to the nearest ten.
29 x 65
2,100

4. Estimate to the nearest ten.
24)442
22

5. Daphne had 75 tulip bulbs to plant. She planted 5 bulbs in a row. How many rows did she plant?

15 rows

Language Practice: Kind of Sentences

Fill in the blanks with the words: *declarative, interrogative, imperative,* or *exclamatory.*

1. Have you ever been on a farm? — interrogative
2. You get to see all kinds of animals on a farm. — declarative
3. "I like pigs the best," said Leeann. — declarative
4. Don't step in the mud. — imperative
5. What a beautiful countryside! — exclamatory
6. Did you know that people work hard on a farm? — interrogative
7. They grow many fruits and vegetables that we eat. — declarative
8. "I love fresh corn!" exclaimed Markel. — exclamatory
9. "Don't make a pig out of yourself," said Markel's mother. — imperative
10. May we come back and visit again? — interrogative

Writing Practice: Write a persuasive paragraph to convince your teacher that you are serious about school.

©Teacher Created Materials, Inc.   117   #3302 Daily Skills Practice—Grades 4–5

Page 118

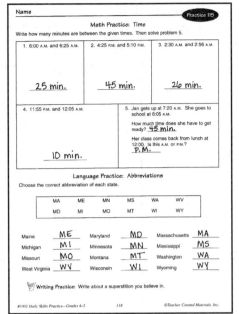

Practice 115

Math Practice: Time

Write how many minutes are between the given times. Then solve problem 5.

1. 6:00 A.M. and 6:25 A.M.	2. 4:25 P.M. and 5:10 P.M.	3. 2:30 A.M. and 2:56 A.M.
25 min.	45 min.	26 min.

4. 11:55 P.M. and 12:05 A.M.	5. Jan gets up at 7:20 A.M. She goes to school at 8:05 A.M.
	How much time does she have to get ready? 45 min.
	Her class comes back from lunch at 12:00. is this A.M. or P.M.?
10 min.	P.M.

Language Practice: Abbreviations

Choose the correct abbreviation of each state.

MA	ME	MN	MS	WA	WV
MD	MI	MO	MT	WI	WY

Maine	ME	Maryland	MD	Massachusetts	MA
Michigan	MI	Minnesota	MN	Mississippi	MS
Missouri	MO	Montana	MT	Washington	WA
West Virginia	WV	Wisconsin	WI	Wyoming	WY

Writing Practice: Write about a superstition you believe in.

Page 119

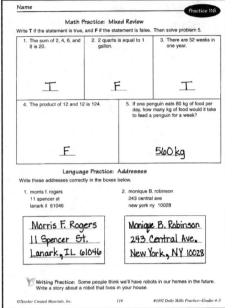

Practice 116

Math Practice: Mixed Review

Write T if the statement is true, and F if the statement is false. Then solve problem 5.

1. The sum of 2, 4, 6, and 8 is 20.	2. 2 quarts is equal to 1 gallon.	3. There are 52 weeks in one year.
T	F	T

4. The product of 12 and 12 is 124.	5. If one penguin eats 80 kg of food per day, how many kg of food would it take to feed a penguin for a week?
F	560 kg

Language Practice: Addresses

Write these addresses correctly in the boxes below.

1. morris f. rogers
11 spencer st
lanark il 61046

2. monique B. robinson
243 central ave
new york ny 10028

Morris F. Rogers	Monique B. Robinson
11 Spencer St.	243 Central Ave.
Lanark, IL 61046	New York, NY 10028

Writing Practice: Some people think we'll have robots in our homes in the future. Write a story about a robot that lives in your house.

Page 120

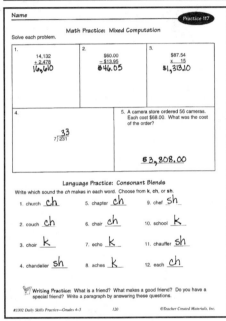

Practice 117

Math Practice: Mixed Computation

Solve each problem.

1. 14,132 + 2,478 = 16,610	2. $60.00 − $13.95 = $46.05	3. $87.54 x 15 = $1,313.10

4. 7)231 = 33	5. A camera store ordered 56 cameras. Each cost $68.00. What was the cost of the order? $3,808.00

Language Practice: Consonant Blends

Write which sound the ch makes in each word. Choose from k, ch, or sh.

1. church ch
2. couch ch
3. choir k
4. chandelier sh
5. chapter ch
6. chair ch
7. echo k
8. aches k
9. chef sh
10. school k
11. chauffer sh
12. each ch

Writing Practice: What is a friend? What makes a good friend? Do you have a special friend? Write a paragraph by answering these questions.

Page 121

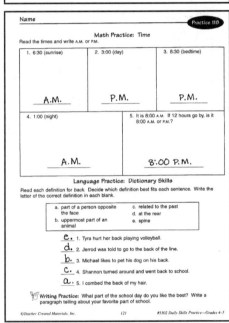

Practice 118

Math Practice: Time

Read the times and write A.M. or P.M.

1. 6:30 (sunrise)	2. 3:00 (day)	3. 8:30 (bedtime)
A.M.	P.M.	P.M.

4. 1:00 (night)	5. It is 8:00 A.M. If 12 hours go by, is it 8:00 A.M. or P.M.?
A.M.	8:00 P.M.

Language Practice: Dictionary Skills

Read each definition for back. Decide which definition best fits each sentence. Write the letter of the correct definition in each blank.

a. part of a person opposite the face	c. related to the past
b. uppermost part of an animal	d. at the rear
	e. spine

e. 1. Tyra hurt her back playing volleyball.
d. 2. Jerrod was told to go to the back of the line.
b. 3. Michael likes to pet his dog on his back.
c. 4. Shannon turned around and went back to school.
a. 5. I combed the back of my hair.

Writing Practice: What part of the school day do you like the best? Write a paragraph telling about your favorite part of school.

Page 122

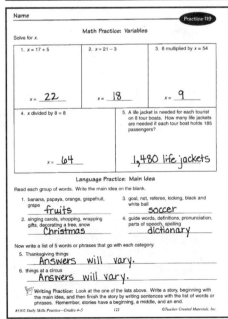

Practice 119

Math Practice: Variables

Solve for x.

1. x = 17 + 5	2. x = 21 − 3	3. 6 multiplied by x = 54
x = 22	x = 18	x = 9

4. x divided by 8 = 8	5. A life jacket is needed for each tourist on 8 tour boats. How many life jackets are needed if each tour boat holds 185 passengers?
x = 64	1,480 life jackets

Language Practice: Main Idea

Read each group of words. Write the main idea on the blank.

1. banana, papaya, orange, grapefruit, grape — fruits
2. singing carols, shopping, wrapping gifts, decorating a tree, snow — Christmas
3. goal, net, referee, kicking, black and white ball — soccer
4. guide words, definitions, pronunciation, parts of speech, spelling — dictionary

Now write a list of 5 words or phrases that go with each category.

5. Thanksgiving things
Answers will vary.
6. things at a circus
Answers will vary.

Writing Practice: Look at the one of the lists above. Write a story, beginning with the main idea, and then finish the story by writing sentences with the list of words or phrases. Remember, stories have a beginning, a middle, and an end.

Page 123

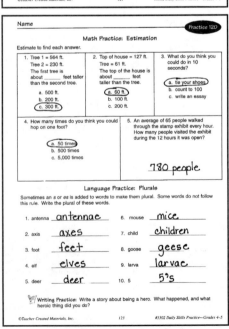

Practice 120

Math Practice: Estimation

Estimate to find each answer.

1. Tree 1 = 564 ft. Tree 2 = 230 ft. The first tree is about ___ feet taller than the second tree. a. 500 ft. b. 200 ft. c. 300 ft.	2. Top of house = 127 ft. Tree = 61 ft. The top of the house is about ___ feet taller than the tree. a. 60 ft. b. 100 ft. c. 200 ft.	3. What do you think you could do in 10 seconds? a. tie your shoes b. count to 100 c. write an essay

4. How many times do you think you could hop on one foot? a. 50 times b. 500 times c. 5,000 times	5. An average of 65 people walked through the stamp exhibit every hour. How many people visited the exhibit during the 12 hours it was open? 780 people

Language Practice: Plurals

Sometimes an s or es is added to words to make them plural. Some words do not follow this rule. Write the plural of these words.

1. antenna — antennae
2. axis — axes
3. foot — feet
4. elf — elves
5. deer — deer
6. mouse — mice
7. child — children
8. goose — geese
9. larva — larvae
10. 5 — 5's

Writing Practice: Write a story about being a hero. What happened, and what heroic thing did you do?

Page 124

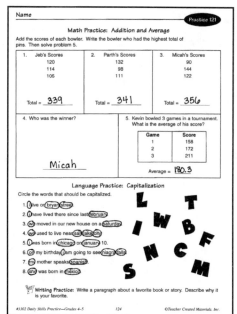

Name _____   Practice 121

Math Practice: Addition and Average

Add the scores of each bowler. Write the bowler who had the highest total of pins. Then solve problem 5.

1. Jeb's Scores	2. Parth's Scores	3. Micah's Scores
120	132	90
114	98	144
105	111	122
Total = 339	Total = 341	Total = 356

4. Who was the winner?	5. Kevin bowled 3 games in a tournament. What is the average of his score?
Micah	Game / Score: 1 / 158, 2 / 172, 3 / 211 — Average = 180.3

Language Practice: Capitalization

Circle the words that should be capitalized.

1. (i) live on (bryan) (street)
2. (i) have lived there since last (february)
3. (we) moved into our new house on a (saturday)
4. (we) used to live near (salt) (lake) (city)
5. (i) was born in (chicago) on (january) 10.
6. (on) my birthday (i) am going to see (niagra) (falls)
7. (my) mother speaks (spanish)
8. (she) was born in (mexico)

L W T I B F N C M S

Writing Practice: Write a paragraph about a favorite book or story. Describe why it is your favorite.

#3302 Daily Skills Practice—Grades 4–5   124   ©Teacher Created Materials, Inc.

Page 125

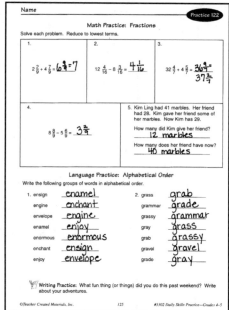

Name _____   Practice 122

Math Practice: Fractions

Solve each problem. Reduce to lowest terms.

1.	2.	3.
$2\frac{2}{9} + 4\frac{7}{9} = 6\frac{9}{9} = 7$	$12\frac{4}{16} - 8\frac{3}{16} = 4\frac{1}{16}$	$32\frac{4}{7} + 4\frac{5}{7} = 36\frac{9}{7} = 37\frac{2}{7}$

4.	5. Kim Ling had 41 marbles. Her friend had 28. Kim gave her friend some of her marbles. Now Kim has 29.
$8\frac{6}{9} - 5\frac{4}{9} = 3\frac{2}{9}$	How many did Kim give her friend? **12 marbles** — How many does her friend have now? **40 marbles**

Language Practice: Alphabetical Order

Write the following groups of words in alphabetical order.

1. ensign	enamel	2. grass	grab
engine	enchant	grammar	grade
envelope	engine	grassy	grammar
enamel	enjoy	gray	grass
enormous	enormous	grab	grassy
enchant	ensign	gravel	gravel
enjoy	envelope	grade	gray

Writing Practice: What fun thing (or things) did you do this past weekend? Write about your adventures.

©Teacher Created Materials, Inc.   125   #3302 Daily Skills Practice—Grades 4–5

Page 126

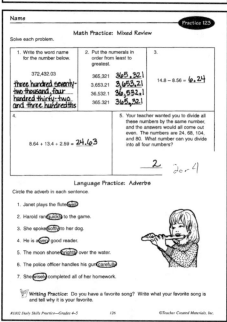

Name _____   Practice 123

Math Practice: Mixed Review

Solve each problem.

1. Write the word name for the number below.	2. Put the numerals in order from least to greatest.	3.
372,432.03 — three hundred seventy-two thousand, four hundred thirty-two and three hundredths	365,321 / 365,321 — 3,653.21 / 3,653.21 — 36,532.1 / 36,532.1 — 365,321 / 365,321	$14.8 - 8.56 = 6.24$

4.	5. Your teacher wanted you to divide all these numbers by the same number, and the answers would all come out even. The numbers are 24, 68, 104, and 80. What number can you divide into all four numbers?
$8.64 + 13.4 + 2.59 = 24.63$	**2** 2 or 4

Language Practice: Adverbs

Circle the adverb in each sentence.

1. Janet plays the flute (well)
2. Harold ran (quickly) to the game.
3. She spoke (softly) to her dog.
4. He is a (very) good reader.
5. The moon shone (brightly) over the water.
6. The police officer handles his gun (carefully)
7. She (wisely) completed all of her homework.

Writing Practice: Do you have a favorite song? Write what your favorite song is and tell why it is your favorite.

#3302 Daily Skills Practice—Grades 4–5   126   ©Teacher Created Materials, Inc.

Page 127

Name _____   Practice 124

Math Practice: Money

Look at the menu. Four families from the neighborhood ordered fast food one evening. Compute the cost of each family's meal, using the menu.

1. Family 1 ordered 2 hot dogs, 2 French fries, 1 potato salad, and 2 sodas.	2. Family 2 ordered 1 hamburger, 3 pizzas, 1 milkshake, and 3 sodas.	3. Family 3 ordered 2 corn dogs, 1 pizza, 2 potato chips, and 3 milkshakes.
Total = $6.40	Total = $8.65	Total = $8.95

4. Family 4 ordered 1 of each item on the menu.	Fast Food Menu
	hot dog $1.25 / hamburger $1.50
	pizza $1.50 / corn dog $1.25
	French fries $1.00 / potato salad $0.90
Total = $10.60	potato chips $0.75 / soft drink $0.50
	milkshake $1.15 / ice cream cone $0.80

Language Practice: Pronouns

Write the pronoun above the underlined word.

1. Marques ran fast. **He** Marques won the race.
2. The boys like to play baseball. **They** The boys play it every Saturday.
3. Mom went to the grocery store. **She** Mom bought food for our lunches.
4. Barbara and I are friends. **We** Barbara and I like to talk on the phone.

Circle the possessive pronoun in each sentence.

5. "That's (my) book," said Emily.
6. Did the baby play with (its) ball?
7. The blue backpack is (mine)
8. The dog ate (its) bone.

Writing Practice: Write a paragraph using the sentence starter below.
The art of being friendly . . .

©Teacher Created Materials, Inc.   127   #3302 Daily Skills Practice—Grades 4–5

Page 128

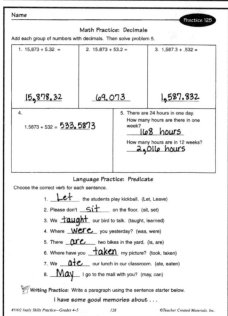

Name _____   Practice 125

Math Practice: Decimals

Add each group of numbers with decimals. Then solve problem 5.

1. $15.873 + 5.32 =$	2. $15.873 + 53.2 =$	3. $1,587.3 + .532 =$
15,878.32	69.073	1,587.832

4.	5. There are 24 hours in one day. How many hours are there in one week?
$1.5873 + 532 = 533.5873$	**168 hours** — How many hours are in 12 weeks? **2,016 hours**

Language Practice: Predicate

Choose the correct verb for each sentence.

1. **Let** the students play kickball. (Let, Leave)
2. Please don't **sit** on the floor. (sit, set)
3. We **taught** our bird to talk. (taught, learned)
4. Where **were** you yesterday? (was, were)
5. There **are** two bikes in the yard. (is, are)
6. Where have you **taken** my picture? (took, taken)
7. We **ate** our lunch in our classroom. (ate, eaten)
8. **May** I go to the mall with you? (may, can)

Writing Practice: Write a paragraph using the sentence starter below.
I have some good memories about . . .

#3302 Daily Skills Practice—Grades 4–5   128   ©Teacher Created Materials, Inc.

Page 129

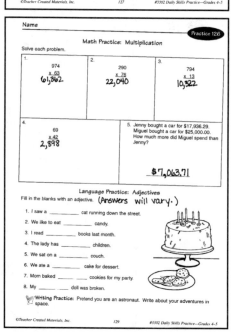

Name _____   Practice 126

Math Practice: Multiplication

Solve each problem.

1. 974 × 63 = 61,362	2. 290 × 76 = 22,040	3. 794 × 13 = 10,322

4. 69 × 42 = 2,898	5. Jenny bought a car for $17,936.29. Miguel bought a car for $25,000.00. How much more did Miguel spend than Jenny? $7,063.71

Language Practice: Adjectives

Fill in the blanks with an adjective. (Answers will vary.)

1. I saw a _____ cat running down the street.
2. We like to eat _____ candy.
3. I read _____ books last month.
4. The lady has _____ children.
5. We sat on a _____ couch.
6. We ate _____ cake for dessert.
7. Mom baked _____ cookies for my party.
8. My _____ doll was broken.

Writing Practice: Pretend you are an astronaut. Write about your adventures in space.

©Teacher Created Materials, Inc.   129   #3302 Daily Skills Practice—Grades 4–5

© Teacher Created Materials, Inc.   227   #3302 Daily Skills Practice—Grades 4–5

Page 130

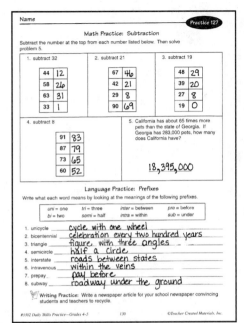

Name _____

Practice 127

Math Practice: Subtraction

Subtract the number at the top from each number listed below. Then solve problem 5.

1. subtract 32		2. subtract 21		3. subtract 19	
44	12	67	46	48	29
58	26	42	21	39	20
63	31	29	8	27	8
33	1	90	69	19	0

4. subtract 8		5. California has about 65 times more pets than the state of Georgia. If Georgia has 283,000 pets, how many does California have?
91	83	
87	79	
73	65	**18,395,000**
60	52	

Language Practice: Prefixes

Write what each word means by looking at the meanings of the following prefixes.

uni = one	tri = three	inter = between	pre = before
bi = two	semi = half	intra = within	sub = under

1. unicycle — cycle with one wheel
2. bicentennial — celebration every two hundred years
3. triangle — figure with three angles
4. semicircle — half a circle
5. interstate — roads between states
6. intravenous — within the veins
7. prepay — pay before
8. subway — roadway under the ground

🖐 **Writing Practice:** Write a newspaper article for your school newspaper convincing students and teachers to recycle.

#3302 Daily Skills Practice—Grades 4–5   130   ©Teacher Created Materials, Inc.

Page 131

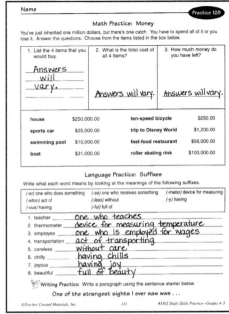

Name _____

Practice 128

Math Practice: Money

You've just inherited one million dollars, but there's one catch. You have to spend all of it or you lose it. Answer the questions. Choose from the items listed in the box below.

1. List the 4 items that you would buy.	2. What is the total cost of all 4 items?	3. How much money do you have left?
Answers will vary.	Answers will vary.	Answers will vary.

house	$250,000.00	ten-speed bicycle	$250.00
sports car	$25,000.00	trip to Disney World	$1,200.00
swimming pool	$15,000.00	fast-food restaurant	$56,000.00
boat	$31,000.00	roller skating rink	$100,000.00

Language Practice: Suffixes

Write what each word means by looking at the meanings of the following suffixes.

(-er) one who does something	(-ee) one who receives something	(-meter) device for measuring
(-ation) act of	(-less) without	(-y) having
(-ous) having	(-ful) full of	

1. teacher — one who teaches
2. thermometer — device for measuring temperature
3. employee — one who is employed for wages
4. transportation — act of transporting
5. careless — without care
6. chilly — having chills
7. joyous — having joy
8. beautiful — full of beauty

🖐 **Writing Practice:** Write a paragraph using the sentence starter below.

One of the strangest sights I ever saw was . . .

©Teacher Created Materials, Inc.   131   #3302 Daily Skills Practice—Grades 4–5

Page 132

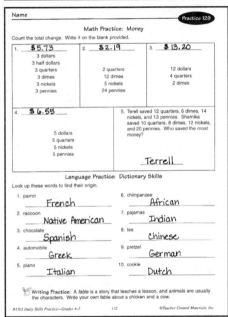

Name _____

Practice 129

Math Practice: Money

Count the total change. Write it on the blank provided.

1. **$5.73**	2. **$2.19**	3. **$13.20**
3 dollars		12 dollars
3 half dollars	2 quarters	4 quarters
3 quarters	12 dimes	2 dimes
3 dimes	5 nickels	
3 nickels	24 pennies	
3 pennies		

4. **$6.55**	5. Terell saved 12 quarters, 6 dimes, 14 nickels, and 13 pennies. Shamika saved 10 quarters, 8 dimes, 12 nickels, and 20 pennies. Who saved the most money?
5 dollars	
5 quarters	
5 nickels	
5 pennies	**Terrell**

Language Practice: Dictionary Skills

Look up these words to find their origin.

1. parrot — French
2. raccoon — Native American
3. chocolate — Spanish
4. automobile — Greek
5. piano — Italian
6. chimpanzee — African
7. pajamas — Indian
8. tea — Chinese
9. pretzel — German
10. cookie — Dutch

🖐 **Writing Practice:** A *fable* is a story that teaches a lesson, and animals are usually the characters. Write your own fable about a chicken and a cow.

#3302 Daily Skills Practice—Grades 4–5   132   ©Teacher Created Materials, Inc.

Page 133

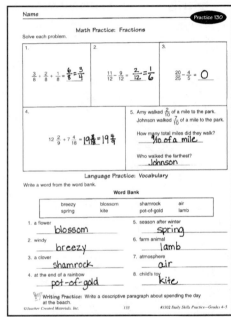

Name _____

Practice 130

Math Practice: Fractions

Solve each problem.

1.	2.	3.
$\frac{3}{8} + \frac{2}{8} + \frac{1}{8} = \frac{6}{8} = \frac{3}{4}$	$\frac{11}{12} - \frac{9}{12} = \frac{2}{12} = \frac{1}{6}$	$\frac{20}{25} - \frac{4}{5} = 0$

4.	5. Amy walked $\frac{2}{10}$ of a mile to the park. Johnson walked $\frac{7}{10}$ of a mile to the park.
$12\frac{2}{9} + 7\frac{4}{18} = 19\frac{8}{18} = 19\frac{4}{9}$	How many total miles did they walk? **9/10 of a mile**
	Who walked the farthest? **Johnson**

Language Practice: Vocabulary

Write a word from the word bank.

Word Bank

breezy	blossom	shamrock	air
spring	kite	pot-of-gold	lamb

1. a flower — blossom
2. windy — breezy
3. a clover — shamrock
4. at the end of a rainbow — pot-of-gold
5. season after winter — spring
6. farm animal — lamb
7. atmosphere — air
8. child's toy — kite

🖐 **Writing Practice:** Write a descriptive paragraph about spending the day at the beach.

©Teacher Created Materials, Inc.   133   #3302 Daily Skills Practice—Grades 4–5

Page 134

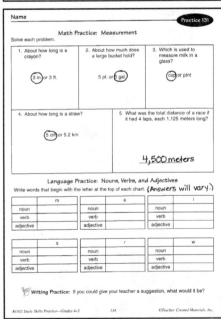

Name _____

Practice 131

Math Practice: Measurement

Solve each problem.

1. About how long is a crayon?	2. About how much does a large bucket hold?	3. Which is used to measure milk in a glass?
(3 in) or 3 ft.	5 pt. or (5 gal.)	(cup) or pint

4. About how long is a straw?	5. What was the total distance of a race if it had 4 laps, each 1,125 meters long?
(5 cm) or 5.2 km	**4,500 meters**

Language Practice: Nouns, Verbs, and Adjectives

Write words that begin with the letter at the top of each chart. **(Answers will vary.)**

	m			a			i
noun			noun			noun	
verb			verb			verb	
adjective			adjective			adjective	

	s			r			w
noun			noun			noun	
verb			verb			verb	
adjective			adjective			adjective	

🖐 **Writing Practice:** If you could give your teacher a suggestion, what would it be?

#3302 Daily Skills Practice—Grades 4–5   134   ©Teacher Created Materials, Inc.

Page 135

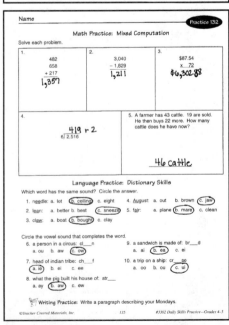

Name _____

Practice 132

Math Practice: Mixed Computation

Solve each problem.

1.	2.	3.
482 658 + 217 **1,357**	3,040 − 1,829 **1,211**	$87.54 x 72 **$6,302.88**

4.	5. A farmer has 43 cattle. 19 are sold. He then buys 22 more. How many cattle does he have now?
419 r 2 6) 2,516	**46 cattle**

Language Practice: Dictionary Skills

Which word has the same sound? Circle the answer.

1. needle: a. lot   (b. ceiling)   c. eight
2. lean: a. better b. best   (c. sneeze)
3. claw: a. boat   (b. bought)   c. clay
4. August: a. out   b. brown   (c. jaw)
5. fair: a. plane   (b. mare)   c. clean

Circle the vowel sound that completes the word.

6. a person in a circus: cl___n
   a. ou   b. aw   (c. ow)
7. head of indian tribe: ch___f
   (a. ie)   b. ei   c. ee
8. what the pig built his house of: str___
   a. ay   (b. aw)   c. ew
9. a sandwich is made of: br___d
   a. ai   (b. ea)   c. ei
10. a trip on a ship: cr___se
    a. oo   b. ou   (c. ui)

🖐 **Writing Practice:** Write a paragraph describing your Mondays.

©Teacher Created Materials, Inc.   135   #3302 Daily Skills Practice—Grades 4–5

Page 136

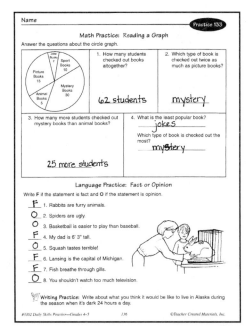

Math Practice: Reading a Graph

Answer the questions about the circle graph.

Circle graph: Joke Books 7, Sport Books 10, Picture Books 15, Mystery Books 30, Animal Books 5

1. How many students checked out books altogether?
62 students

2. Which type of book is checked out twice as much as picture books?
mystery

3. How many more students checked out mystery books than animal books?
25 more students

4. What is the least popular book?
jokes
Which type of book is checked out the most?
mystery

Language Practice: Fact or Opinion

Write F if the statement is fact and O if the statement is opinion.

F 1. Rabbits are furry animals.
O 2. Spiders are ugly.
O 3. Basketball is easier to play than baseball.
F 4. My dad is 6' 3" tall.
O 5. Squash tastes terrible!
F 6. Lansing is the capital of Michigan.
F 7. Fish breathe through gills.
O 8. You shouldn't watch too much television.

✏️ **Writing Practice:** Write about what you think it would be like to live in Alaska during the season when it's dark 24 hours a day.

#3302 Daily Skills Practice—Grades 4–5   136   ©Teacher Created Materials, Inc.

Page 137

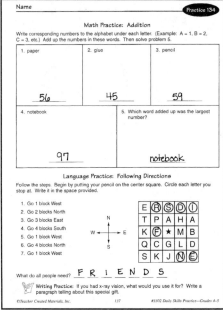

Math Practice: Addition

Write corresponding numbers to the alphabet under each letter. (Example: A = 1, B = 2, C = 3, etc.) Add up the numbers in these words. Then solve problem 5.

1. paper **56**

2. glue **45**

3. pencil **59**

4. notebook **97**

5. Which word added up was the largest number?
notebook

Language Practice: Following Directions

Follow the steps. Begin by putting your pencil on the center square. Circle each letter you stop at. Write it in the space provided.

1. Go 1 block West
2. Go 2 blocks North
3. Go 3 blocks East
4. Go 4 blocks South
5. Go 1 block West
6. Go 4 blocks North
7. Go 1 block West

Grid:
E	R	S	D	I
T	P	A	H	A
K	F	★	M	B
Q	C	G	L	D
S	K	J	N	E

What do all people need? **F R I E N D S**

✏️ **Writing Practice:** If you had x-ray vision, what would you use it for? Write a paragraph telling about this special gift.

©Teacher Created Materials, Inc.   137   #3302 Daily Skills Practice—Grades 4–5

Page 138

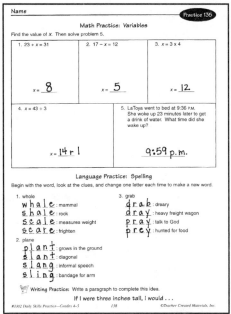

Math Practice: Variables

Find the value of x. Then solve problem 5.

1. $23 \div x = 31$ $x =$ **8**

2. $17 - x = 12$ $x =$ **5**

3. $x = 3 \times 4$ $x =$ **12**

4. $x = 43 \div 3$ $x =$ **14 r 1**

5. LaToya went to bed at 9:36 P.M. She woke up 23 minutes later to get a drink of water. What time did she wake up?
9:59 p.m.

Language Practice: Spelling

Begin with the word, look at the clues, and change one letter each time to make a new word.

1. whole
w h a l e : mammal
s h a l e : rock
s c a l e : measures weight
s c a r e : frighten

2. plane
p l a n t : grows in the ground
s l a n t : diagonal
s l a n g : informal speech
s l i n g : bandage for arm

3. grab
d r a b : dreary
d r a y : heavy freight wagon
p r a y : talk to God
p r e y : hunted for food

✏️ **Writing Practice:** Write a paragraph to complete this idea.
If I were three inches tall, I would . . .

#3302 Daily Skills Practice—Grades 4–5   138   ©Teacher Created Materials, Inc.

Page 139

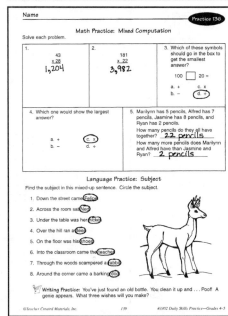

Math Practice: Mixed Computation

Solve each problem.

1. $43 \times 28 =$ **1,204**

2. $181 \times 22 =$ **3,982**

3. Which of these symbols should go in the box to get the smallest answer?
$100 \ \square \ 20 =$
a. +   c. x
b. –   **d. ÷**

4. Which one would show the largest answer?
a. +   **c. x**
b. –   d. ÷

5. Marilynn has 5 pencils, Alfred has 7 pencils, Jasmine has 8 pencils, and Ryan has 2 pencils.
How many pencils do they all have together? **22 pencils**
How many more pencils does Marilynn and Alfred have than Jasmine and Ryan? **2 pencils**

Language Practice: Subject

Find the subject in this mixed-up sentence. Circle the subject.

1. Down the street came (Felipe).
2. Across the room sat (Nedra).
3. Under the table was her (kitten).
4. Over the hill ran a (deer).
5. On the floor was his (shoes).
6. Into the classroom came the (teacher).
7. Through the woods scampered a (rabbit).
8. Around the corner came a barking (dog).

✏️ **Writing Practice:** You've just found an old bottle. You clean it up and . . . Poof! A genie appears. What three wishes will you make?

©Teacher Created Materials, Inc.   139   #3302 Daily Skills Practice—Grades 4–5

Page 140

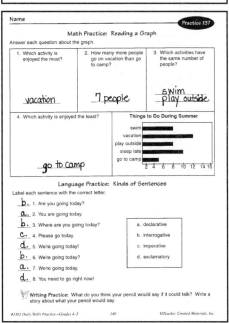

Math Practice: Reading a Graph

Answer each question about the graph.

1. Which activity is enjoyed the most?
vacation

2. How many more people go on vacation than go to camp?
7 people

3. Which activities have the same number of people?
swim play outside

4. Which activity is enjoyed the least?
go to camp

Things to Do During Summer
(bar graph: swim, vacation, play outside, sleep late, go to camp — scale 2 4 6 8 10 12 14 16)

Language Practice: Kinds of Sentences

Label each sentence with the correct letter.

b. 1. Are you going today?
a. 2. You are going today.
b. 3. Where are you going today?
c. 4. Please go today.
d. 5. We're going today!
b. 6. We're going today?
a. 7. We're going today.
d. 8. You need to go right now!

a. declarative
b. interrogative
c. imperative
d. exclamatory

✏️ **Writing Practice:** What do you think your pencil would say if it could talk? Write a story about what your pencil would say.

#3302 Daily Skills Practice—Grades 4–5   140   ©Teacher Created Materials, Inc.

Page 141

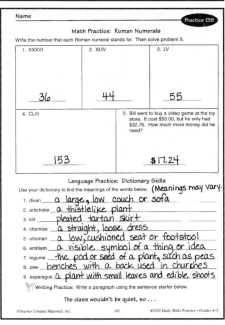

Math Practice: Roman Numerals

Write the number that each Roman numeral stands for. Then solve problem 5.

1. XXXVI **36**

2. XLIV **44**

3. LV **55**

4. CLIII **153**

5. Bill went to buy a video game at the toy store. It cost $50.00, but he only had $32.76. How much more money did he need?
$17.24

Language Practice: Dictionary Skills

Use your dictionary to find the meanings of the words below. **(Meanings may vary.)**

1. divan — **a large, low couch or sofa**
2. artichoke — **a thistlelike plant**
3. kilt — **pleated tartan skirt**
4. chemise — **a straight, loose dress**
5. ottoman — **a low, cushioned seat or footstool**
6. emblem — **a visible symbol of a thing or idea**
7. legume — **the pod or seed of a plant, such as peas**
8. pew — **benches with a back used in churches**
9. asparagus — **a plant with small leaves and edible shoots**

✏️ **Writing Practice:** Write a paragraph using the sentence starter below.
The class wouldn't be quiet, so . . .

©Teacher Created Materials, Inc.   141   #3302 Daily Skills Practice—Grades 4–5

Page 142

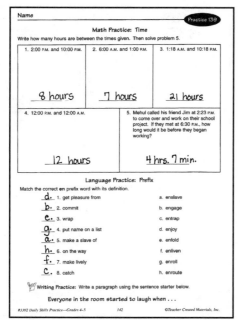

Name

Practice 139

Math Practice: Time

Write how many hours are between the times given. Then solve problem 5.

1. 2:00 P.M. and 10:00 P.M.	2. 6:00 A.M. and 1:00 P.M.	3. 1:18 A.M. and 10:18 P.M.
8 hours	_7 hours_	_21 hours_

4. 12:00 P.M. and 12:00 A.M.	5. Mehul called his friend Jim at 2:23 P.M. to come over and work on their school project. If they met at 6:30 P.M., how long would it be before they began working?
12 hours	_4 hrs. 7 min._

Language Practice: Prefix

Match the correct en prefix word with its definition.

_d._ 1. get pleasure from   a. enslave
_b._ 2. commit   b. engage
_e._ 3. wrap   c. entrap
_g._ 4. put name on a list   d. enjoy
_a._ 5. make a slave of   e. enfold
_h._ 6. on the way   f. enliven
_f._ 7. make lively   g. enroll
_c._ 8. catch   h. enroute

Writing Practice: Write a paragraph using the sentence starter below.

Everyone in the room started to laugh when . . .

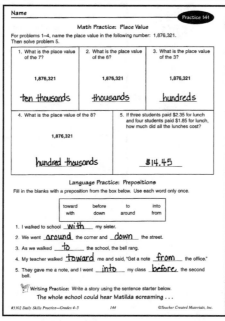 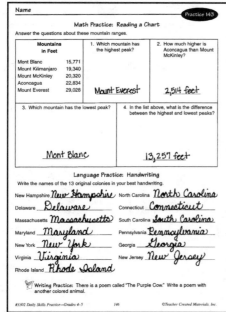

#3302 Daily Skills Practice—Grades 4–5   142   ©Teacher Created Materials, Inc.

Page 143

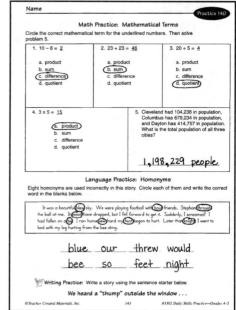

Name

Practice 140

Math Practice: Mathematical Terms

Circle the correct mathematical term for the underlined numbers. Then solve problem 5.

1. $10 - 8 = \underline{2}$	2. $23 + 23 = \underline{46}$	3. $20 \div 5 = \underline{4}$
a. product	a. product	a. product
b. sum	(b. sum)	b. sum
(c. difference)	c. difference	c. difference
d. quotient	d. quotient	(d. quotient)

4. $3 \times 5 = \underline{15}$	5. Cleveland had 104,238 in population, Columbus has 679,234 in population, and Dayton has 414,757 in population. What is the total population of all three cities?
(a. product) b. sum c. difference d. quotient	_1,198,229 people_

Language Practice: Homonyms

Eight homonyms are used incorrectly in this story. Circle each of them and write the correct word in the blanks below.

It was a beautiful (blew) sky. We were playing football with (hour) friends. Stephan (threw) the ball at me. It (seed) have dropped, but I fell forward to get it. Suddenly, I screamed! I had fallen on a (bee) I ran home (sew) hard my (feat) began to hurt. Later that (knight) I went to bed with my leg hurting from the bee sting.

blue _our_ _threw_ _would_
bee _so_ _feet_ _night_

Writing Practice: Write a story using the sentence starter below.

We heard a "thump" outside the window . . .

©Teacher Created Materials, Inc.   143   #3302 Daily Skills Practice—Grades 4–5

Page 144

Name

Practice 141

Math Practice: Place Value

For problems 1–4, name the place value in the following number: 1,876,321. Then solve problem 5.

1. What is the place value of the 7?	2. What is the place value of the 6?	3. What is the place value of the 3?
1,876,321	1,876,321	1,876,321
ten thousands	_thousands_	_hundreds_

4. What is the place value of the 8?	5. If three students paid $2.35 for lunch and four students paid $1.85 for lunch, how much did all the lunches cost?
1,876,321	
hundred thousands	_$14.45_

Language Practice: Prepositions

Fill in the blanks with a preposition from the box below. Use each word only once.

toward	before	to	into
with	down	around	from

1. I walked to school _with_ my sister.
2. We went _around_ the corner and _down_ the street.
3. As we walked _to_ the school, the bell rang.
4. My teacher walked _toward_ me and said, "Get a note _from_ the office."
5. They gave me a note, and I went _into_ my class _before_ the second bell.

Writing Practice: Write a story using the sentence starter below.

The whole school could hear Matilda screaming . . .

#3302 Daily Skills Practice—Grades 4–5   144   ©Teacher Created Materials, Inc.

Page 145

Name

Practice 142

Math Practice: Rounding

Round to the nearest whole number. Then solve problem 5.

1. $4.3 =$ _4_	2. $9.78 =$ _10_	3. $85.03 =$ _85_

4. $7.1 =$ _7_	5. Merlin walked 2.3 miles, Arnold walked 7.5 miles, William walked 3.1 miles, and Franklin walked 8.7 miles. Round each to the nearest whole number. How many miles did they walk in all?
	22 miles

Language Practice: Verb

Fill in the chart with the correct form of the verb.

Present	Past	Past Participle
sing	_sang_	sung
ring	rang	rung
read	read	_read_
think	_thought_	thought
walk	walked	walked
take	_took_	taken
sit	sat	_sat_
blow	_blew_	blown

Writing Practice: Write a story using the sentence starter below.

In the middle of the night, I was thirsty. When I got up, I couldn't believe my eyes . . .

©Teacher Created Materials, Inc.   145   #3302 Daily Skills Practice—Grades 4–5

Page 146

Name

Practice 143

Math Practice: Reading a Chart

Answer the questions about these mountain ranges.

Mountains in Feet		1. Which mountain has the highest peak?	2. How much higher is Aconcagua than Mount McKinley?
Mont Blanc	15,771		
Mount Kilimanjaro	19,340		
Mount McKinley	20,320		
Aconcagua	22,834	_Mount Everest_	_2,514 feet_
Mount Everest	29,028		

3. Which mountain has the lowest peak?	4. In the list above, what is the difference between the highest and lowest peaks?
Mont Blanc	_13,257 feet_

Language Practice: Handwriting

Write the names of the 13 original colonies in your best handwriting.

New Hampshire _New Hampshire_   North Carolina _North Carolina_
Delaware _Delaware_   Connecticut _Connecticut_
Massachusetts _Massachusetts_   South Carolina _South Carolina_
Maryland _Maryland_   Pennsylvania _Pennsylvania_
New York _New York_   Georgia _Georgia_
Virginia _Virginia_   New Jersey _New Jersey_
Rhode Island _Rhode Island_

Writing Practice: There is a poem called "The Purple Cow." Write a poem with another colored animal.

#3302 Daily Skills Practice—Grades 4–5   146   ©Teacher Created Materials, Inc.

Page 147

Name

Practice 144

Math Practice: Fractions

Write each problem as a fraction. Then solve problem 5.

1. $.15 = \dfrac{15}{100} = \dfrac{3}{20}$	2. $3.6 = 3\dfrac{6}{10} = 3\dfrac{3}{5}$	3. $7.52 = 7\dfrac{52}{100} = 7\dfrac{13}{25}$

4. $1.07 = 1\dfrac{7}{100}$	5. There were 15 yards of material bought to make curtains for the school play. The total cost was $135.00. How much did each yard of material cost?
	_$9.00_

Language Practice: Antonym

Write an antonym for each word. _(Answers will vary.)_

1. above _____   9. large _____
2. add _____   10. up _____
3. easy _____   11. fat _____
4. leave _____   12. long _____
5. happy _____   13. clean _____
6. heavy _____   14. hard _____
7. many _____   15. shiny _____
8. brave _____   16. wet _____

Writing Practice: If you were a talk show host, what two guests would you invite to be on your show? What two questions would you ask them?

©Teacher Created Materials, Inc.   147   #3302 Daily Skills Practice—Grades 4–5

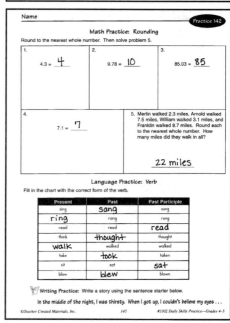

Page 148

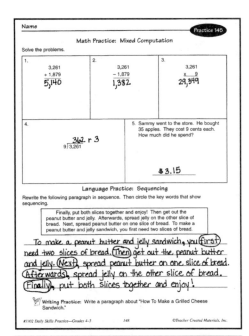

Page 149

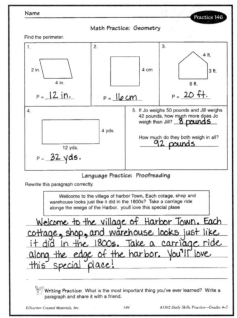

Page 150

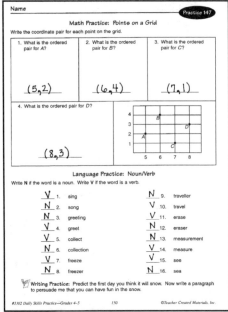

Page 151

Page 152

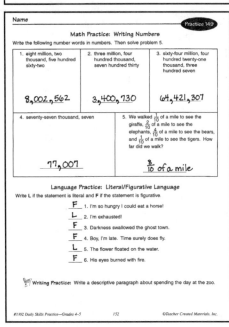

Page 153

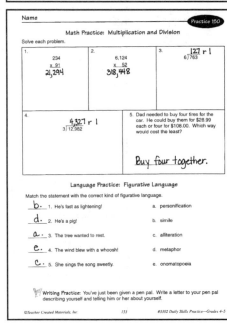

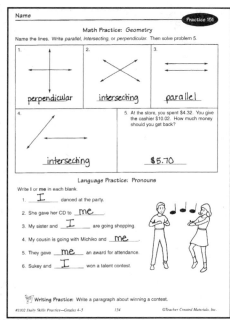

Practice 151

Name

Math Practice: Geometry

Name the lines. Write *parallel*, *intersecting*, or *perpendicular*. Then solve problem 5.

| 1. perpendicular | 2. intersecting | 3. parallel |
| 4. intersecting | 5. At the store, you spent $4.32. You give the cashier $10.02. How much money should you get back? $5.70 | |

Language Practice: Pronouns

Write *I* or *me* in each blank.

1. _I_ danced at the party.
2. She gave her CD to _me_.
3. My sister and _I_ are going shopping.
4. My cousin is going with Michiko and _me_.
5. They gave _me_ an award for attendance.
6. Sukey and _I_ won a talent contest.

✍️ **Writing Practice:** Write a paragraph about winning a contest.

#3302 Daily Skills Practice—Grades 4–5   154   ©Teacher Created Materials, Inc.

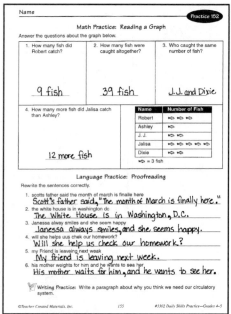

Practice 152

Name

Math Practice: Reading a Graph

Answer the questions about the graph below.

| 1. How many fish did Robert catch?   9 fish | 2. How many fish were caught altogether?   39 fish | 3. Who caught the same number of fish?   J.J. and Dixie |
| 4. How many more fish did Jalisa catch than Ashley?   12 more fish | 5. | |

Name	Number of Fish
Robert	🐟 🐟 🐟
Ashley	🐟
J. J.	🐟 🐟
Jalisa	🐟 🐟 🐟 🐟 🐟
Dixie	🐟 🐟

🐟 = 3 fish

Language Practice: Proofreading

Rewrite the sentences correctly.

1. scotts father said the month of march is finalle here
   Scott's father said, "The month of March is finally here."
2. the white house is in washington dc
   The White House is in Washington, D.C.
3. Janessa alway smiles and she seem happy
   Janessa always smiles, and she seems happy.
4. will she helps uus chek our homework?
   Will she help us check our homework?
5. my Friend is leaving next weak
   My friend is leaving next week.
6. his mother weights for him and he wants to sea her
   His mother waits for him, and he wants to see her.

✍️ **Writing Practice:** Write a paragraph about why you think we need our circulatory system.

©Teacher Created Materials, Inc.   155   #3302 Daily Skills Practice—Grades 4–5

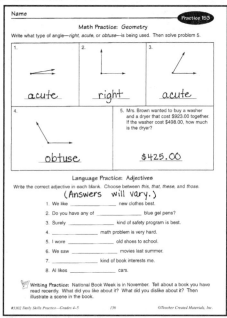

Practice 153

Name

Math Practice: Geometry

Write what type of angle—*right*, *acute*, or *obtuse*—is being used. Then solve problem 5.

| 1. acute | 2. right | 3. acute |
| 4. obtuse | 5. Mrs. Brown wanted to buy a washer and a dryer that cost $923.00 together. If the washer cost $498.00, how much is the dryer? $425.00 | |

Language Practice: Adjectives

Write the correct adjective in each blank. Choose between *this*, *that*, *these*, and *those*.

(Answers will vary.)

1. We like _____ new clothes best.
2. Do you have any of _____ blue gel pens?
3. Surely _____ kind of safety program is best.
4. _____ math problem is very hard.
5. I wore _____ old shoes to school.
6. We saw _____ movies last summer.
7. _____ kind of book interests me.
8. Al likes _____ cars.

✍️ **Writing Practice:** National Book Week is in November. Tell about a book you have read recently. What did you like about it? What did you dislike about it? Then illustrate a scene in the book.

#3302 Daily Skills Practice—Grades 4–5   156   ©Teacher Created Materials, Inc.

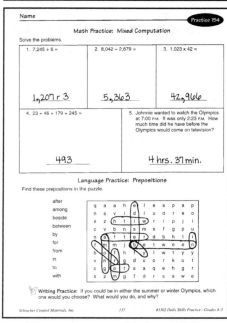

Practice 154

Name

Math Practice: Mixed Computation

Solve the problems.

| 1. $7,245 \div 6 =$ 1,207 r 3 | 2. $8,042 - 2,679 =$ 5,363 | 3. $1,023 \times 42 =$ 42,966 |
| 4. $23 + 46 + 179 + 245 =$ 493 | 5. Johnnie wanted to watch the Olympics at 7:00 P.M. It was only 2:23 P.M. How much time did he have before the Olympics would come on television?   4 hrs. 37 min. | |

Language Practice: Prepositions

Find these prepositions in the puzzle.

after
among
beside
between
by
for
from
in
to
with

q	a	a	h	e	l	e	a	p	a
n	s	v	i	d	l	u	d	r	e
x	z	h	t	i	w	r	i	p	j
c	v	b	n	s	m	s	f	g	p
n	a	f	t	e	r	d	b	h	l
m	m	i	b	e	t	w	e	e	n
b	o	n	i	r	v	l	w	t	y
v	n	g	d	u	o	r	k	u	
n	g	o	t	s	a	q	e	h	g
x	z	m	g	f	d	r	s	a	w

✍️ **Writing Practice:** If you could be in either the summer or winter Olympics, which one would you choose? What would you do, and why?

©Teacher Created Materials, Inc.   157   #3302 Daily Skills Practice—Grades 4–5

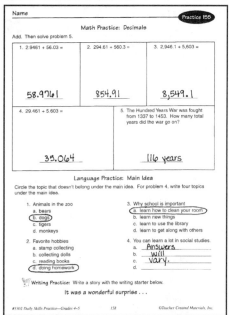

Practice 155

Name

Math Practice: Decimals

Add. Then solve problem 5.

| 1. $2.9461 + 56.03 =$ 58.9761 | 2. $294.61 + 560.3 =$ 854.91 | 3. $2,946.1 + 5,603 =$ 8,549.1 |
| 4. $29.461 + 5.603 =$ 35.064 | 5. The Hundred Years War was fought from 1337 to 1453. How many total years did the war go on?   116 years | |

Language Practice: Main Idea

Circle the topic that doesn't belong under the main idea. For problem 4, write four topics under the main idea.

1. Animals in the zoo
   a. bears
   b. dogs
   c. tigers
   d. monkeys

2. Favorite hobbies
   a. stamp collecting
   b. collecting dolls
   c. reading books
   d. doing homework

3. Why school is important
   a. learn how to clean your room
   b. learn new things
   c. learn to use the library
   d. learn to get along with others

4. You can learn a lot in social studies.
   a. Answers will vary.
   b.
   c.
   d.

✍️ **Writing Practice:** Write a story with the writing starter below.

It was a wonderful surprise . . .

#3302 Daily Skills Practice—Grades 4–5   158   ©Teacher Created Materials, Inc.

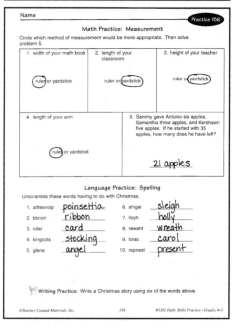

Practice 156

Name

Math Practice: Measurement

Circle which method of measurement would be more appropriate. Then solve problem 5.

| 1. width of your math book   ruler or yardstick | 2. length of your classroom   ruler or yardstick | 3. height of your teacher   ruler or yardstick |
| 4. length of your arm   ruler or yardstick | 5. Sammy gave Antonio six apples, Samantha three apples, and Kershawn five apples. If he started with 35 apples, how many does he have left?   21 apples | |

Language Practice: Spelling

Unscramble these words having to do with Christmas.

1. aittesnoip — poinsettia
2. bbrion — ribbon
3. cdar — card
4. kingcots — stocking
5. glena — angel
6. shigei — sleigh
7. lloyh — holly
8. rewaht — wreath
9. lorac — carol
10. repnest — present

✍️ **Writing Practice:** Write a Christmas story using six of the words above.

©Teacher Created Materials, Inc.   159   #3302 Daily Skills Practice—Grades 4–5

Page 160

Practice 157

Math Practice: Reading a Graph

Answer the questions about the graph.

1. On which days were 3 students absent?	2. Which day had the most students absent?	3. Were more students absent on Wednesday or Thursday?
Monday Thursday	Tuesday	Thursday

4. How many more students were absent on Tuesday than Wednesday?	Number of Students Absent
2 more students	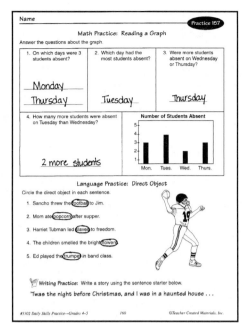 Mon. Tues. Wed. Thurs.

Language Practice: Direct Object

Circle the direct object in each sentence.

1. Sancho threw the (football) to Jim.
2. Mom ate (popcorn) after supper.
3. Harriet Tubman led (slaves) to freedom.
4. The children smelled the bright (flowers).
5. Ed played the (trumpet) in band class.

✏ **Writing Practice:** Write a story using the sentence starter below.

'Twas the night before Christmas, and I was in a haunted house . . .

#3302 Daily Skills Practice—Grades 4–5   160   ©Teacher Created Materials, Inc.

Page 161

Name
Practice 158

Math Practice: Writing Numbers

For problems 1 and 2, write the words in numbers. For problems 3 and 4, write the numbers in words. Then solve problem 5.

1. six million, one hundred four thousand, two hundred fifty-five	2. two hundred seventy-two thousand, six hundred ninety	3. 13,765
6,104,255	272,690	thirteen thousand, seven hundred sixty-five

4. 1,206,400	5. You and three friends are buying a present for your teacher and will need to pay equal amounts. The total is $20.44. How much will each pay?
one million, two hundred six thousand, four hundred	$5.11

Language Practice: Story Comprehension

Answer the questions about the story.

> Amelia Earhart is known for being the first woman pilot to fly across the Atlantic Ocean. She made this famous flight in 1932. She received an award after this famous flight. The award was the Distinguished Flying Cross, and she was the first woman to have received the award. In 1937, she began a flight that would take her around the world. Her plane disappeared over the Pacific Ocean, and to this day, no one knows what happened to her.

1. What did Amelia Earhart do in 1932? She flew across the Atlantic Ocean.
2. Name the award she received? She received the Distinguished Flying Cross.
3. What did Amelia Earhart attempt to do in 1937? She tried to fly around the world.
4. How did she die? No one knows how she died. She disappeared.

✏ **Writing Practice:** Write what you think the differences are in planes during Amelia Earhart's day and the jets that are used today.

©Teacher Created Materials, Inc.   161   #3302 Daily Skills Practice—Grades 4–5

Page 162

Name
Practice 159

Math Practice: Fractions

Subtract these fractions with like denominators. Then solve problem 5.

1. $\frac{7}{8} - \frac{2}{8} = \frac{5}{8}$	2. $\frac{12}{15} - \frac{3}{15} = \frac{9}{15} = \frac{3}{5}$	3. $8\frac{3}{4} - \frac{1}{4} = 8\frac{2}{4} = 8\frac{1}{2}$

4. $5\frac{9}{12} - 4\frac{1}{12} = 1\frac{8}{12} = 1\frac{2}{3}$	5. Javier wants to buy CDs with his birthday money. He received $30.00 from his grandma. If each CD cost $14.97, how many CD's can he buy? 2 CDs

Language Practice: Analogies   (Answers may vary.)

Complete each analogy.

1. Orange is to fruit as almond is to _nut_.
2. Foot is to shoe and _hand_ is to glove.
3. Remote is to _television_ as joystick is to video game.
4. Snow is to shovel as _dirt_ is to back-hoe.
5. _Cold_ is to hot as black is to white.
6. Stripes are to tigers as spots are to _Dalmatians_.

✏ **Writing Practice:** Write a paragraph using the title below.

Things I Remember Most About Kindergarten

#3302 Daily Skills Practice—Grades 4–5   162   ©Teacher Created Materials, Inc.

Page 163

Name
Practice 160

Math Practice: Variables

Fill in the blanks. Then solve problem 5.

1. If $6 + a = 10$, then $a =$ 4	2. If $20 - b = 15$, then $b =$ 5	3. If $4 \times c = 40$, then $c =$ 10

4. If $50 \div d = 25$, then $d =$ 2	5. Your neighbor Mr. Jones is paying you to walk his dog Tubbs. If he gives you $0.50 a day, how many days will it take to earn $10.00? 20 days

Language Practice: Verbs

Complete each sentence by adding a compound verb. (Answers will vary.)

1. The rabbits _____ and _____ in the forest.
2. The squirrels _____ and _____ up the tree.
3. The snake _____ and _____ along the ground.
4. The lions _____ and _____ in their cages.
5. The baby birds _____ and _____ in their nests.

✏ **Writing Practice:** Do you have a favorite poster on the wall in your room at home? Do you collect things? Write a descriptive paragraph describing your room.

©Teacher Created Materials, Inc.   163   #3302 Daily Skills Practice—Grades 4–5

Page 164

Name
Practice 161

Math Practice: Decimals

For problems 1 and 2, write each decimal in numbers. For problems 3 and 4, write each decimal in words. Then solve problem 5.

1. ninety-eight and six tenths	2. two thousand forty and eighty-two hundredths	3. 114.7
98.6	2,040.82	one hundred fourteen and seven tenths

4. 26.54	5. Juanita has to be at school at 8:00. If it takes her 15 minutes to get dressed, 12 minutes to eat breakfast, 5 minutes to brush her teeth, and 8 minutes to get to school, what time does she need to get up?
twenty-six and fifty-four hundredths	7:20 a.m.

Language Practice: Alphabetical Order

Put the names of Santa's reindeer in alphabetical order.

Dasher	Blitzen
Dancer	Comet
Prancer	Cupid
Vixen	Dancer
Comet	Dasher
Cupid	Donner
Donner	Prancer
Blitzen	Rudolph
Rudolph	Vixen

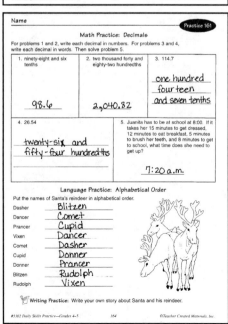

✏ **Writing Practice:** Write your own story about Santa and his reindeer.

#3302 Daily Skills Practice—Grades 4–5   164   ©Teacher Created Materials, Inc.

Page 165

Name
Practice 162

Math Practice: Fractions

Change to mixed numerals. Then solve problem 5.

1. $\frac{17}{4} =$ $4\frac{1}{4}$	2. $\frac{23}{5} =$ $4\frac{3}{5}$	3. $\frac{47}{7} =$ $6\frac{5}{7}$

4. $\frac{99}{10} =$ $9\frac{9}{10}$	5. Tom played football for his school team. He made three touchdowns. His friend made two touchdowns. How many points did they score in the game? (Hint: touchdown = 6 points) 30 points

Language Practice: Sentence/Fragment

Add the correct end mark to each complete sentence. Write a F if the sentence is incomplete.

1. Go fishing with Dad   F
2. The girls watching a scary movie   F
3. Hamilton read six books this month   .
4. He can teach his parrot to talk   .
5. A man in the boat   F
6. A million stars in the sky   F
7. We went to English class. We worked on our language sentences   .
8. Our teacher gave us treats for Valentine's Day   .

✏ **Writing Practice:** Write your own fairy tale about a frog and a princess.

©Teacher Created Materials, Inc.   165   #3302 Daily Skills Practice—Grades 4–5

Page 166

Name _____ Practice 163

Math Practice: Geometry

Fill in the missing answer and draw a picture of the shape. Then solve problem 5.

1. A pentagon has **5** sides.	2. A hexagon has **6** sides.	3. An octagon has **8** sides.

4. Kelly, DeWayne, Jerika, and Edgar went to a masquerade party. They were dressed as a lion, tiger, bear, and cougar, but not in that order. Jerika was not the cougar, and Edgar's costume did not have a long tail. Kelly was either the tiger or the bear. What were each person's costume?

Kelly = **tiger**
DeWayne = **cougar**
Jerika = **lion**
Edgar = **bear**

Language Practice: Consonant Blends

Add two different blends (scr, spl, shr, spr, str, thr) to each word ending to make two new words.

1. **scr** eam **str** eam
2. **spr** ing **str** ing
3. **spl** ash **thr** ash
4. **shr** ill **thr** ill
5. **shr** ead **thr** ead
6. **scr** ap **str** ap
7. **spr** ee **thr** ee
8. **scr** ew **thr** ew

Writing Practice: There are only a few types of animals that live in the Arctic. Write about how you would like or dislike living in the Arctic.

#3302 Daily Skills Practice—Grades 4–5   166   ©Teacher Created Materials, Inc.

Page 167

Name _____ Practice 164

Math Practice: Sets

Look at the following set of whole numbers through ten {0, 1, 2, 3, 4, 5, 6, 7, 8, 9, 10}. Using this set, list the sets below. Then solve problem 5.

1. even numbers	2. odd numbers	3. numbers divisible by 5
(2,4,6,8,10)	(1,3,5,7,9)	(5,10)

4. numbers divisible by three	5. Bobbie is going to a party. He has to leave by 5:00. Before he can go, he has to finish his chores (15 min.), walk his sister to her friend's house (5 min.), get air put in his bike tire (10 min.), and finish his homework (25 min.). If he gets home from school at 3:30, how much time is left to get dressed?
(3,6,9)	**35 min.**

Language Practice: Fact or Opinion

Write **F** if the statement is fact and **O** if the statement is opinion.

O 1. Piglets are cute baby pigs.
O 2. People may live in space someday.
F 3. An oyster has a shell.
O 4. There are aliens on Mars.
O 5. Libraries are fun to visit.
F 6. Water is necessary for humans to live.
O 7. Strawberries are delicious.
O 8. It is fun to play in the snow.

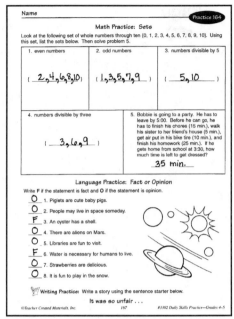

Writing Practice: Write a story using the sentence starter below.

It was so unfair . . .

©Teacher Created Materials, Inc.   167   #3302 Daily Skills Practice—Grades 4–5

Page 168

Name _____ Practice 165

Math Practice: Variables

For problems 1–4, fill in the blanks. Then solve problem 5.

1. If 10 + e = 32, then e = **22**	2. If 21 − f = 10, then f = **11**	3. If 6 x g = 48, then g = **8**

4. If 99 ÷ h = 11, then h = **9**	5. The perimeter of a square is 20 inches. How long is each side? **5 inches**

Language Practice: Commas

Write a sentence that corresponds with each comma rule. Be sure to use the comma correctly.   **(Answers will vary.)**

1. Use a comma to separate items in a list.
2. Use a comma to set off direct quotes.
3. Use a comma to separate the names of cities and states.
4. Use a comma to set off a direct address.
5. Use a comma and a connecting word to connect two clauses.

Writing Practice: There are over 250,000 kinds of flowers. Flowers are given to people sometimes to help them feel better. Write a story about either getting flowers or giving flowers and how it made you feel.

#3302 Daily Skills Practice—Grades 4–5   168   ©Teacher Created Materials, Inc.

Page 169

Name _____ Practice 166

Math Practice: Percents/Fractions

For problems 1–4, write each percent as a fraction. Make sure to reduce each answer. Then solve problem 5.

1. $17\% = \frac{17}{100}$	2. $35\% = \frac{35}{100} = \frac{7}{20}$	3. $75\% = \frac{75}{100} = \frac{3}{4}$

4. $20\% = \frac{20}{100} = \frac{1}{5}$	5. The perimeter of a triangle is 58 meters. One side is 18 meters long, and another side is 25 meters long. How long is the third side? **15 meters**

Language Practice: Possessives

Write the correct possessive in the blank.

1. The cat has a toy mouse. Evan played with the **cat's** toy mouse.
2. My sisters have dolls. My **sisters'** dolls are fun to play with.
3. Sue Ellen is on the basketball team. We saw **Sue Ellen's** team play yesterday.
4. Her uncle has a bicycle shop. Her **uncle's** bicycle shop is on Third Street.
5. The pencils belong to the students. The **students'** pencils were on their desks.
6. The birds sing merrily. The **birds'** song is sweet to hear.

Writing Practice: Write a paragraph using the sentence starter below.

"Well, it's about time you came . . ."

©Teacher Created Materials, Inc.   169   #3302 Daily Skills Practice—Grades 4–5

Page 170

Name _____ Practice 167

Math Practice: Decimals/Fractions

Write the following decimals as a fraction. Then solve problem 5.

1. $0.67 = \frac{67}{100}$	2. $0.9 = \frac{9}{10}$	3. $0.212 = \frac{212}{1,000}$ or $\frac{53}{250}$

4. $0.49 = \frac{49}{100}$	5. A grasshopper can jump 3 feet high and 20 times its length. If a grasshopper is 3.5 inches long, how far can it jump? **70 inches**

Language Practice: Abbreviations

Unscramble the name of the state. Then match it to its abbreviation.

Nickname	State	Abbreviations		Abbreviations
1. Heart of Dixie	(AAAAMBL) **Alabama**	**AL**		IA
2. Last Frontier	(AAAKSL) **Alaska**	**AK**		ID
3. Grand Canyon State	(AANROZI) **Arizona**	**AZ**		IN
4. Land of Opportunity	(AAASKRNS) **Arkansas**	**AR**		IL
5. Gem State	(IOHAD) **Idaho**	**ID**		AZ
6. Land of Lincoln	(IIILSLNO) **Illinois**	**IL**		AR
7. Hoosier State	(IIAANND) **Indiana**	**IN**		AL
8. Hawkeye State	(IAOW) **Iowa**	**IA**		AK

Writing Practice: Hawaii is the only state that is a group of islands. Write a story about being alone on an island.

#3302 Daily Skills Practice—Grades 4–5   170   ©Teacher Created Materials, Inc.

Page 171

Name _____ Practice 168

Math Practice: Fractions

For problems 1–4, add the mixed numbers. Then solve problem 5.

1. $8\frac{2}{7} + 4\frac{3}{7} = 12\frac{5}{7}$	2. $5\frac{2}{5} + 6\frac{1}{5} = 11\frac{3}{5}$	3. $9\frac{3}{8} + 1\frac{4}{8} = 10\frac{7}{8}$

4. $6\frac{2}{9} + 6\frac{5}{9} = 12\frac{7}{9}$	5. Jimmy lives $\frac{1}{2}$ of a mile away from the baseball field. If he walks there in the morning, back home for lunch, back to the field, and then back home for dinner, how far has he walked? **1$\frac{1}{8}$ miles**

Language Practice: Analogies

Complete each analogy.   **(Answers will vary.)**

1. dog is to puppy as cow is to _____
2. ship is to sail as car is to _____
3. book is to read as music is to _____
4. on is to off as here is to _____
5. come is to came as some is to _____
6. pencil is to paper as paintbrush is to _____
7. tan is to brown as pink is to _____
8. milk is to cup as coffee is to _____

Writing Practice: Create a newspaper article with the heading below.

Extra! Extra! Read All About It!

©Teacher Created Materials, Inc.   171   #3302 Daily Skills Practice—Grades 4–5

Page 166, **Page 167**, **Page 168**, **Page 169**, **Page 170**, **Page 171**

Page 172

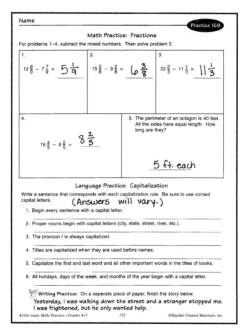

Math Practice: Fractions

For problems 1–4, subtract the mixed numbers. Then solve problem 5.

1. $12\frac{8}{9} - 7\frac{7}{9} =$ **$5\frac{1}{9}$**	2. $15\frac{5}{8} - 9\frac{2}{8} =$ **$6\frac{3}{8}$**	3. $22\frac{2}{3} - 11\frac{1}{3} =$ **$11\frac{1}{3}$**
4. $16\frac{4}{5} - 8\frac{2}{5} =$ **$8\frac{2}{5}$**	5. The perimeter of an octagon is 40 feet. All the sides have equal length. How long are they? **5 ft. each**	

Language Practice: Capitalization

Write a sentence that corresponds with each capitalization rule. Be sure to use correct capital letters. **(Answers will vary.)**

1. Begin every sentence with a capital letter.

2. Proper nouns begin with capital letters (city, state, street, river, etc.).

3. The pronoun I is always capitalized.

4. Titles are capitalized when they are used before names.

5. Capitalize the first and last word and all other important words in the titles of books.

6. All holidays, days of the week, and months of the year begin with a capital letter.

Writing Practice: On a seperate piece of paper, finish the story below.
Yesterday, I was walking down the street and a stranger stopped me. I was frightened, but he only wanted help.

#3302 Daily Skills Practice—Grades 4–5   172   ©Teacher Created Materials, Inc.

Page 173

Math Practice: Measurement

For problems 1–4, fill in the blanks. Then solve problem 5.

1. $\frac{2}{3}$ yd. = **2** feet	2. $\frac{3}{4}$ hr. = **45** minutes	3. $\frac{1}{2}$ doz. = **6** eggs
4. $\frac{1}{4}$ ft. = **3** inches	5. A jar of candy has 592 pieces in it. Each bag of candy used to fill up the jar contained 30 pieces. How many bags were needed to fill the jar? **20 bags** How many extra pieces of candy were left over? **8 pieces**	

Language Practice: Handwriting

Write this poem in your best handwriting.

Bugs
I like bugs.
Black bugs, green bugs,
Bad bugs, mean bugs,
Any kind of bug.
A bug in a rug, a bug in the grass,
A bug on the sidewalk, a bug in a glass,
I like bugs.
Big bugs, fat bugs,
Shiny bugs, round bugs,
Lady bugs, buggy bugs,
I like bugs.
—Unknown

(title) **Students' writing will vary.**

Writing Practice: Write your own poem about an animal or insect that you like.

©Teacher Created Materials, Inc.   173   #3302 Daily Skills Practice—Grades 4–5

Page 174

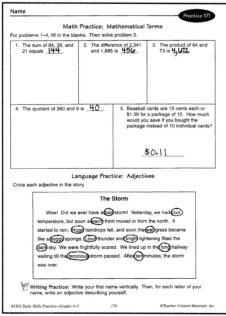

Math Practice: Mathematical Terms

For problems 1–4, fill in the blanks. Then solve problem 5.

1. The sum of 84, 39, and 21 equals **144**.	2. The difference of 2,341 and 1,885 is **456**.	3. The product of 64 and 73 is **4,672**.
4. The quotient of 360 and 9 is **40**.	5. Baseball cards are 15 cents each or $1.39 for a package of 10. How much would you save if you bought the package instead of 10 individual cards? **$0.11**	

Language Practice: Adjectives

Circle each adjective in the story.

The Storm

Wow! Did we ever have a ~bad~ storm! Yesterday, we had ~cool~ temperature, but soon a ~warm~ front moved in from the north. It started to rain. ~Huge~ raindrops fell, and soon the ~wet~ grass became like a ~soggy~ sponge. ~Loud~ thunder and ~bright~ lightening filled the ~dark~ sky. We were frightfully scared. We lined up in the ~long~ hallway waiting till the ~ferocious~ storm passed. After ~ten~ minutes, the storm was over.

Writing Practice: Write your first name vertically. Then, for each letter of your name, write an adjective describing yourself.

#3302 Daily Skills Practice—Grades 4–5   174   ©Teacher Created Materials, Inc.

Page 175

Math Practice: Mixed Review

For problems 1–4, fill in the blanks. Then solve problem 5.

1. The average of 6, 18, and 12 is **12**.	2. In October, there are four full weeks or **3** days.	3. The time between 10:25 A.M. and 11:10 A.M. is **45** minutes.
4. One-third of the number 12 is **4**.	5. In the classroom, there are 24 students. $\frac{1}{3}$ are reading, $\frac{1}{2}$ are doing math, and the rest are working on spelling. How many are working on spelling? **4 students**	

Language Practice: Rhyming Words

Fill in the blanks of this poem with a word that rhymes. **(Answers may vary.)**

Groundhog Day

This furry friend might come out once a year
To keep his shadow if the day is **clear**
And on this very special Groundhog Day
If his shadow is seen, winter will **stay**
For six more long weeks we'll have to keep warm,
But if it's cloudy, his shadow's not there
There'll soon be warm weather and days will be **fair**
So please, Mr. Sun, just this one day,
Find a big dark cloud—and stay **away**!
—Unknown

Writing Practice: Write a story about a surprising turn of events when the groundhog sees his shadow.

©Teacher Created Materials, Inc.   175   #3302 Daily Skills Practice—Grades 4–5

Page 176

Math Practice: Reading a Chart

Look at the chart. Answer the questions using the information from the chart.

1. Who is older, Jesse Jackson or Muhammad Ali? **Jesse Jackson**	2. How many years younger is Ali than Rosa Parks? **29 years**	3. How many years older is Rosa Parks than Bill Cosby? **24 years**

4. Jesse Owens was famous for running in track and field events. He was born in 1913 and died in 1980. How old was he when he died? **67 years old**	Black American	Born
	Bill Cosby	1937
	Rosa Parks	1913
	Shirley Chisholm	1924
	Jesse Jackson	1941
	Muhammad Ali	1942

Language Practice: Cause and Effect

Underline the cause in each sentence.

1. When Sally listens in class, she makes better grades.

2. We'll go outside for P.E. because the weather is nice.

3. If Betsy cleans her room, she'll be able to go to the mall.

4. April talked on the phone and ordered a pizza.

5. Jeff tried out for the lead in *Romeo and Juliet* and was chosen to play the part of Romeo.

6. We went to the ballgame, when my uncle came for a visit.

Writing Practice: Margaret Thatcher once said, "Being powerful is like being a lady. If you have to tell people you are, you aren't." What do you think she meant by that? Do you agree with her?

#3302 Daily Skills Practice—Grades 4–5   176   ©Teacher Created Materials, Inc.

Page 177

Math Practice: Fractions

For problems 1–4, fill in the blanks. Then solve problem 5.

1. $\frac{1}{8}$ of 16 = **2**	2. $\frac{1}{3}$ of 24 = **8**	3. $\frac{3}{4}$ of 12 = **9**
4. $\frac{1}{7}$ of 21 = **3**	5. It is 398 miles to Aunt Edna's house. The train goes 80 miles per hour. About how many hours will it take to get to her house? **5 hours**	

Language Practice: Sequencing

Read the story. Number the sentences so that they are in correct order.

The Camping Trip

Dad told Ben that their scout camping trip would be on Friday. He told him to pack his bags. Ben thought about what he should pack. Then he packed his clothes, his camping gear, his scout manual, his football, and his sleeping bag. After he finished packing, he told his dad he was ready to go! Finally, on Friday, they left for the scout camping trip.

5 Ben and his dad went camping.
1 Dad told Ben about the camping trip.
2 Dad told Ben to pack.
4 Ben packed his clothes.
3 Ben decided what to pack.

Writing Practice: Your are going to make a time capsule with stuff about yourself. What would you put in your time capsule, and why?

©Teacher Created Materials, Inc.   177   #3302 Daily Skills Practice—Grades 4–5

© Teacher Created Materials, Inc.   235   #3302 Daily Skills Practice—Grades 4–5

Page 178

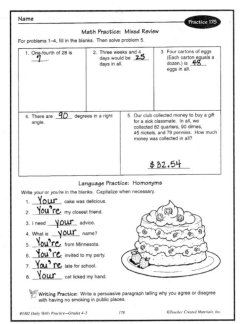

Name _____ Practice 175

Math Practice: Mixed Review

For problems 1–4, fill in the blanks. Then solve problem 5.

1. One-fourth of 28 is **7**.

2. Three weeks and 4 days would be **25** days in all.

3. Four cartons of eggs (Each carton equals a dozen.) is **48** eggs in all.

4. There are **90** degrees in a right angle.

5. Our club collected money to buy a gift for a sick classmate. In all, we collected 82 quarters, 90 dimes, 45 nickels, and 79 pennies. How much money was collected in all?

$32.54

Language Practice: Homonyms

Write *your* or *you're* in the blanks. Capitalize when necessary.

1. **Your** cake was delicious.
2. **You're** my closest friend.
3. I need **your** advice.
4. What is **your** name?
5. **You're** from Minnesota.
6. **You're** invited to my party.
7. **You're** late for school.
8. **Your** cat licked my hand.

Writing Practice: Write a persuasive paragraph telling why you agree or disagree with having no smoking in public places.

#3302 Daily Skills Practice—Grades 4–5   178   ©Teacher Created Materials, Inc.

Page 179

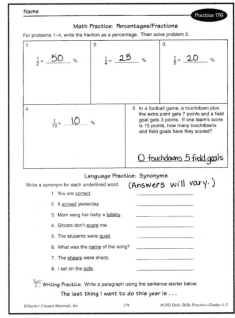

Name _____ Practice 176

Math Practice: Percentages/Fractions

For problems 1–4, write the fraction as a percentage. Then solve problem 5.

1. $\frac{1}{2}$ = **50** %

2. $\frac{1}{4}$ = **25** %

3. $\frac{1}{5}$ = **20** %

4. $\frac{1}{10}$ = **10** %

5. In a football game, a touchdown plus the extra point gets 7 points and a field goal gets 3 points. If one team's score is 15 points, how many touchdowns and field goals have they scored?

0 touchdowns 5 field goals

Language Practice: Synonyms

Write a synonym for each underlined word. **(Answers will vary.)**

1. You are <u>correct</u>. _____
2. It <u>arrived</u> yesterday. _____
3. Mom sang her baby a <u>lullaby</u>. _____
4. Ghosts don't <u>scare</u> me. _____
5. The students were <u>quiet</u>. _____
6. What was the <u>name</u> of the song? _____
7. The <u>shears</u> were sharp. _____
8. I sat on the <u>sofa</u>. _____

Writing Practice: Write a paragraph using the sentence starter below.
The last thing I want to do this year is . . .

©Teacher Created Materials, Inc.   179   #3302 Daily Skills Practice—Grades 4–5

Page 180

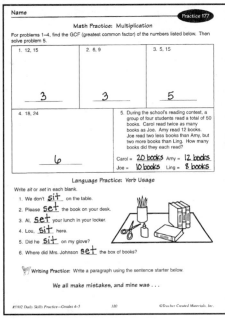

Name _____ Practice 177

Math Practice: Multiplication

For problems 1–4, find the GCF (greatest common factor) of the numbers listed below. Then solve problem 5.

1. 12, 15   **3**

2. 6, 9   **3**

3. 5, 15   **5**

4. 18, 24   **6**

5. During the school's reading contest, a group of four students read a total of 50 books. Carol read twice as many books as Joe. Amy read 12 books. Joe read two less books than Amy, but two more books than Ling. How many books did they each read?

Carol = **20 books**   Amy = **12 books**
Joe = **10 books**   Ling = **8 books**

Language Practice: Verb Usage

Write *sit* or *set* in each blank.

1. We don't **sit** on the table.
2. Please **set** the book on your desk.
3. Al, **set** your lunch in your locker.
4. Lou, **sit** here.
5. Did he **sit** on my glove?
6. Where did Mrs. Johnson **set** the box of books?

Writing Practice: Write a paragraph using the sentence starter below.

We all make mistakes, and mine was . . .

#3302 Daily Skills Practice—Grades 4–5   180   ©Teacher Created Materials, Inc.

Page 181

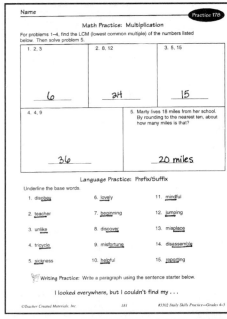

Name _____ Practice 178

Math Practice: Multiplication

For problems 1–4, find the LCM (lowest common multiple) of the numbers listed below. Then solve problem 5.

1. 2, 3   **6**

2. 8, 12   **24**

3. 5, 15   **15**

4. 4, 9   **36**

5. Marty lives 18 miles from her school. By rounding to the nearest ten, about how many miles is that?

20 miles

Language Practice: Prefix/Suffix

Underline the base words.

1. dis<u>obey</u>   6. <u>love</u>ly   11. <u>mind</u>ful
2. <u>teach</u>er   7. <u>begin</u>ning   12. <u>jump</u>ing
3. un<u>like</u>   8. <u>discover</u>   13. mis<u>place</u>
4. tri<u>cycle</u>   9. mis<u>fortune</u>   14. dis<u>assemble</u>
5. <u>sick</u>ness   10. <u>help</u>ful   15. <u>report</u>ing

Writing Practice: Write a paragraph using the sentence starter below.

I looked everywhere, but I couldn't find my . . .

©Teacher Created Materials, Inc.   181   #3302 Daily Skills Practice—Grades 4–5

Page 182

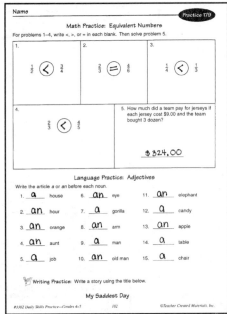

Name _____ Practice 179

Math Practice: Equivalent Numbers

For problems 1–4, write <, >, or = in each blank. Then solve problem 5.

1. $\frac{1}{2}$ **<** $\frac{3}{4}$

2. $\frac{2}{3}$ **=** $\frac{4}{6}$

3. $\frac{1}{4}$ **<** $\frac{1}{3}$

4. $\frac{2}{3}$ **<** $\frac{4}{5}$

5. How much did a team pay for jerseys if each jersey cost $9.00 and the team bought 3 dozen?

$324.00

Language Practice: Adjectives

Write the article *a* or *an* before each noun.

1. **a** house   6. **an** eye   11. **an** elephant
2. **an** hour   7. **a** gorilla   12. **a** candy
3. **an** orange 8. **an** arm   13. **an** apple
4. **an** aunt   9. **a** man   14. **a** table
5. **a** job   10. **an** old man 15. **a** chair

Writing Practice: Write a story using the title below.

My Saddest Day

#3302 Daily Skills Practice—Grades 4–5   182   ©Teacher Created Materials, Inc.

Page 183

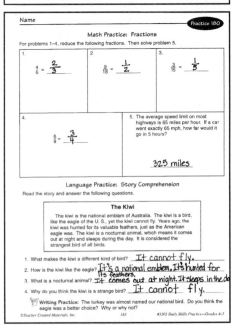

Name _____ Practice 180

Math Practice: Fractions

For problems 1–4, reduce the following fractions. Then solve problem 5.

1. $\frac{4}{6}$ = **$\frac{2}{3}$**

2. $\frac{9}{18}$ = **$\frac{1}{2}$**

3. $\frac{3}{15}$ = **$\frac{1}{5}$**

4. $\frac{6}{8}$ = **$\frac{3}{4}$**

5. The average speed limit on most highways is 65 miles per hour. If a car went exactly 65 mph, how far would it go in 5 hours?

325 miles

Language Practice: Story Comprehension

Read the story and answer the following questions.

The Kiwi

The kiwi is the national emblem of Australia. The kiwi is a bird, like the eagle of the U.S., yet the kiwi cannot fly. Years ago, the kiwi was hunted for its valuable feathers, just as the American eagle was. The kiwi is a nocturnal animal, which means it comes out at night and sleeps during the day. It is considered the strangest bird of all birds.

1. What makes the kiwi a different kind of bird? **It cannot fly.**
2. How is the kiwi like the eagle? **It's a national emblem. It's hunted for its feathers.**
3. What is a nocturnal animal? **It comes out at night. It sleeps in the day.**
4. Why do you think the kiwi is a strange bird? **It cannot fly.**

Writing Practice: The turkey was almost named our national bird. Do you think the eagle was a better choice? Why or why not?

©Teacher Created Materials, Inc.   183   #3302 Daily Skills Practice—Grades 4–5

Page 184

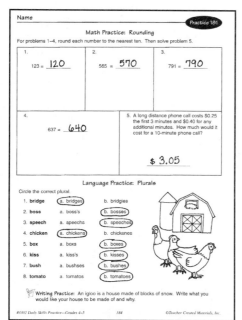

Name

Practice 181

Math Practice: Rounding

For problems 1–4, round each number to the nearest ten. Then solve problem 5.

1. $123 = $ __120__	2. $565 = $ __570__	3. $791 = $ __790__
4. $637 = $ __640__		5. A long distance phone call costs $0.25 the first 3 minutes and $0.40 for any additional minutes. How much would it cost for a 10-minute phone call? **$ 3.05**

Language Practice: Plurals

Circle the correct plural.

1. **bridge** (a. bridges) b. bridgies
2. **boss** a. boss's (b. bosses)
3. **speech** a. speechs (b. speeches)
4. **chicken** (a. chickens) b. chickenes
5. **box** a. boxs (b. boxes)
6. **kiss** a. kiss's (b. kisses)
7. **bush** a. bushses (b. bushes)
8. **tomato** a. tomatos (b. tomatoes)

Writing Practice: An igloo is a house made of blocks of snow. Write what you would like your house to be made of and why.

#3302 Daily Skills Practice—Grades 4–5   184   ©Teacher Created Materials, Inc.

Page 185

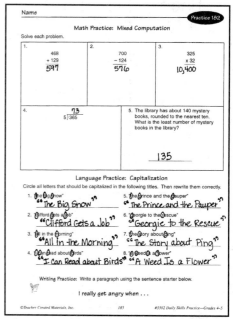

Name

Practice 182

Math Practice: Mixed Computation

Solve each problem.

1. 468 + 129 = **597**	2. 700 − 124 = **576**	3. 325 × 32 = **10,400**
4. $5)\overline{365}$ = **73**		5. The library has about 140 mystery books, rounded to the nearest ten. What is the least number of mystery books in the library? **135**

Language Practice: Capitalization

Circle all letters that should be capitalized in the following titles. Then rewrite them correctly.

1. "the big snow" "The Big Snow"
2. "clifford gets a job" "Clifford Gets a Job"
3. "all in the morning" "All In the Morning"
4. "i can read about birds" "I Can Read about Birds"
5. "the prince and the pauper" "The Prince and the Pauper"
6. "georgie to the rescue" "Georgie to the Rescue"
7. "the story about ping" "The Story about Ping"
8. "a weed is a flower" "A Weed Is a Flower"

Writing Practice: Write a paragraph using the sentence starter below.

I really get angry when . . .

©Teacher Created Materials, Inc.   185   #3302 Daily Skills Practice—Grades 4–5

Page 186

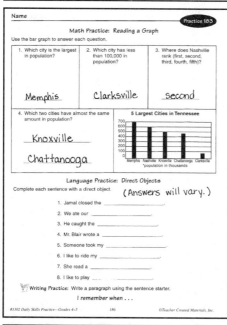

Name

Practice 183

Math Practice: Reading a Graph

Use the bar graph to answer each question.

1. Which city is the largest in population? **Memphis**	2. Which city has less than 100,000 in population? **Clarksville**	3. Where does Nashville rank (first, second, third, fourth, fifth)? **second**
4. Which two cities have almost the same amount in population? **Knoxville** **Chattanooga**		**5 Largest Cities in Tennessee** [bar graph] Memphis Nashville Knoxville Chattanooga Clarksville *population in thousands

Language Practice: Direct Objects

Complete each sentence with a direct object.   (Answers will vary.)

1. Jamal closed the _____.
2. We ate our _____.
3. He caught the _____.
4. Mr. Blair wrote a _____.
5. Someone took my _____.
6. I like to ride my _____.
7. She read a _____.
8. I like to play _____.

Writing Practice: Write a paragraph using the sentence starter.

I remember when . . .

#3302 Daily Skills Practice—Grades 4–5   186   ©Teacher Created Materials, Inc.

Page 187

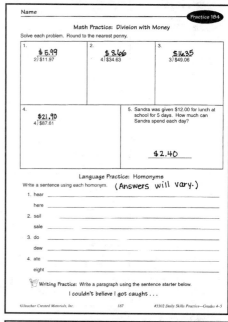

Name

Practice 184

Math Practice: Division with Money

Solve each problem. Round to the nearest penny.

1. $2)\overline{\$11.97}$ = **$5.99**	2. $4)\overline{\$34.63}$ = **$8.66**	3. $3)\overline{\$49.06}$ = **$16.35**
4. $4)\overline{\$87.61}$ = **$21.90**		5. Sandra was given $12.00 for lunch at school for 5 days. How much can Sandra spend each day? **$2.40**

Language Practice: Homonyms

Write a sentence using each homonym.   (Answers will vary.)

1. hear _____
   here _____
2. sail _____
   sale _____
3. do _____
   dew _____
4. ate _____
   eight _____

Writing Practice: Write a paragraph using the sentence starter below.

I couldn't believe I got caught . . .

©Teacher Created Materials, Inc.   187   #3302 Daily Skills Practice—Grades 4–5

Page 188

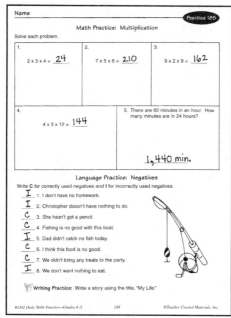

Name

Practice 185

Math Practice: Multiplication

Solve each problem.

1. $2 \times 3 \times 4 = $ **24**	2. $7 \times 5 \times 6 = $ **210**	3. $9 \times 2 \times 9 = $ **162**
4. $4 \times 3 \times 12 = $ **144**		5. There are 60 minutes in an hour. How many minutes are in 24 hours? **1,440 min.**

Language Practice: Negatives

Write C for correctly used negatives and I for incorrectly used negatives.

__I__ 1. I don't have no homework.
__I__ 2. Christopher doesn't have nothing to do.
__C__ 3. She hasn't got a pencil.
__C__ 4. Fishing is no good with this boat.
__I__ 5. Dad didn't catch no fish today.
__C__ 6. I think this food is no good.
__C__ 7. We didn't bring any treats to the party.
__I__ 8. We don't want nothing to eat.

Writing Practice: Write a story using the title, "My Life."

#3302 Daily Skills Practice—Grades 4–5   188   ©Teacher Created Materials, Inc.

Page 189

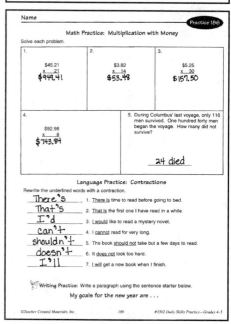

Name

Practice 186

Math Practice: Multiplication with Money

Solve each problem.

1. $45.21 × 21 = **$949.41**	2. $3.82 × 14 = **$53.48**	3. $5.25 × 30 = **$157.50**
4. $92.98 × 8 = **$743.84**		5. During Columbus' last voyage, only 116 men survived. One hundred forty men began the voyage. How many did not survive? **24 died**

Language Practice: Contractions

Rewrite the underlined words with a contraction.

There's 1. There is time to read before going to bed.
That's 2. That is the first one I have read in a while.
I'd 3. I would like to read a mystery novel.
can't 4. I cannot read for very long.
shouldn't 5. The book should not take but a few days to read.
doesn't 6. It does not look too hard.
I'll 7. I will get a new book when I finish.

Writing Practice: Write a paragraph using the sentence starter below.

My goals for the new year are . . .

©Teacher Created Materials, Inc.   189   #3302 Daily Skills Practice—Grades 4–5

Page 190

Name _____
Practice 187

Math Practice: Mean

For problems 1–4, find the averages of these test scores. Then solve problem 5.

1. Billy: 85, 88, 95	2. Jorge: 99, 100, 81	3. Joanne: 89, 89, 93
89.3	93.3	90.3

4. Jaquarius: 90, 80, 88	5. Simon and his friend Wayne set up a lemonade stand. A cup of lemonade cost $0.25 each. They made $5.00. How many cups of lemonade did they sell?
86	20 cups

Language Practice: Compound Words

Make a compound word by adding a beginning or an ending to the words below.

(Answers will vary.)

1. _____ground   5. _____him   9. sun_____
2. grand_____   6. _____age   10. _____ball
3. book_____   7. every_____   11. _____man
4. _____plane   8. with_____   12. home_____

🐿 **Writing Practice:** Imagine waking up and finding out you're 10 feet tall. Write a story about your adventures.

#3302 Daily Skills Practice—Grades 4–5   190   ©Teacher Created Materials, Inc.

Page 191

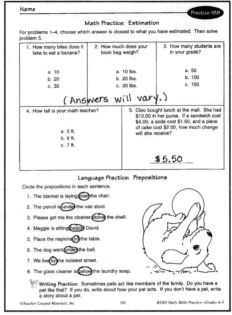

Name _____
Practice 188

Math Practice: Estimation

For problems 1–4, choose which answer is closest to what you have estimated. Then solve problem 5.

1. How many bites does it take to eat a banana?	2. How much does your book bag weigh?	3. How many students are in your grade?
a. 10 b. 20 c. 30	a. 10 lbs. b. 20 lbs. c. 30 lbs.	a. 50 b. 100 c. 150

(Answers will vary.)

4. How tall is your math teacher?	5. Cleo bought lunch at the mall. She had $13.00 in her purse. If a sandwich cost $4.00, a soda cost $1.50, and a piece of cake cost $2.00, how much change will she receive?
a. 5 ft. b. 6 ft. c. 7 ft.	$5.50

Language Practice: Prepositions

Circle the prepositions in each sentence.

1. The blanket is laying (over) the chair.
2. The pencil is (under) the oak stool.
3. Please get me the cleaner (above) the shelf.
4. Maggie is sitting (beside) David.
5. Place the napkins (on) the table.
6. The dog went (under) the ball.
7. We live (by) the noisiest street.
8. The glass cleaner is (below) the laundry soap.

🐿 **Writing Practice:** Sometimes pets act like members of the family. Do you have a pet like that? If you do, write about how your pet acts. If you don't have a pet, write a story about a pet.

©Teacher Created Materials, Inc.   191   #3302 Daily Skills Practice—Grades 4–5

Page 192

Name _____
Practice 189

Math Practice: Fractions/Decimals/Percents

For problems 1–4, fill in the blanks on the chart. Then solve problem 5.

1. Fraction = $\frac{33}{100}$ Decimal = .33 Percent = 33%	2. Fraction = $\frac{54}{100}$ Decimal = .54 Percent = 54%	3. Fraction = $\frac{77}{100}$ Decimal = .77 Percent = 77%

4. Fraction = $\frac{12}{100}$ Decimal = .12 Percent = 12%	5. A television Joe wanted cost $185.00. He noticed the store put it on sale at 25% off. How much would the television cost after the discount?
	$138.75

Language Practice: Compound Sentences

Add a connecting word and finish each sentence to make a compound sentence.

1. My best friend is nice, _____ Answers will vary.
2. Our cat likes to lay on the couch, _____
3. My math teacher is strict, _____
4. Mac sings in the shower, _____
5. Harry wants to go bowling, _____

🐿 **Writing Practice:** Write a story using the sentence starter below.
I went ice skating on the pond, when suddenly I heard a cracking sound . . .

#3302 Daily Skills Practice—Grades 4–5   192   ©Teacher Created Materials, Inc.

Page 193

Name _____
Practice 190

Math Practice: Mathematical Terms

For problems 1–4, circle the letter of its meaning. Then solve problem 5.

1. deci-	2. centi-	3. milli-
a. hundredth b. millionth c. tenth ✓ d. thousandth	a. hundredth ✓ b. millionth c. tenth d. thousandth	a. hundredth b. millionth c. tenth d. thousandth ✓

4. micro-	5. The baseball team sold 45 cans of soda, 24 bars of candy, and 10 bags of popcorn. They all cost $0.50. How much money did the team make?
a. hundredth b. millionth ✓ c. tenth d. thousandth	$39.50

Language Practice: Abbreviation/Punctuation

Circle the abbreviations that need periods.

(Mr) (pm) CIA COD CD
MD (BC) TN (oz) FL
TV (qt) (St) RSVP (Rd)
km (Dr) USA (US) (in)

🐿 **Writing Practice:** Alexander had a no good, very bad day. Write about your no good, very bad day.

©Teacher Created Materials, Inc.   193   #3302 Daily Skills Practice—Grades 4–5

Page 194

Name _____
Practice 191

Math Practice: Addition with Money

Solve each problem.

1. $654.88 + $98.92 =	2. $9,832.11 + $903.45 =	3. $54.00 + $87.38 =
$753.80	$10,735.56	$141.38

4. $99.99 + $11.11 =	5. Amanda bought 5 shirts in the mall for $9.99 each. How much did she spend in all?
$111.10	$49.95

Language Practice: Parts of Speech

Match each part of speech with its definition.

b. 1. noun   a. describe noun or pronoun
e. 2. pronoun   b. names a person, place, thing, or idea
d. 3. verb   c. connects words
a. 4. adjective   d. express action or state of being
g. 5. adverb   e. takes the place of a noun
h. 6. preposition   f. shows emotion or surprise
f. 7. interjection g. describes a verb
c. 8. conjunction   h. relates a noun to another word

🐿 **Writing Practice:** You're walking on the beach and you look down and see a bottle. It has a message inside. Write about what it says.

#3302 Daily Skills Practice—Grades 4–5   194   ©Teacher Created Materials, Inc.

Page 195

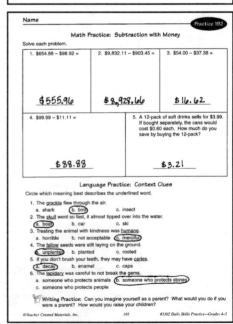

Name _____
Practice 192

Math Practice: Subtraction with Money

Solve each problem.

1. $654.88 – $98.92 =	2. $9,832.11 – $903.45 =	3. $54.00 – $37.38 =
$555.96	$8,928.66	$16.62

4. $99.99 – $11.11 =	5. A 12-pack of soft drinks sells for $3.99. If bought separately, the cans would cost $0.60 each. How much do you save by buying the 12-pack?
$88.88	$3.21

Language Practice: Context Clues

Circle which meaning best describes the underlined word.

1. The grackle flew through the air.
   a. shark   b. bird ✓   c. insect
2. The skull went so fast, it almost tipped over into the water.
   a. boat ✓   b. car   c. ski
3. Treating the animal with kindness was humane.
   a. horrible   b. not acceptable   c. merciful ✓
4. The fallow seeds were still laying on the ground.
   a. unplanted ✓   b. planted   c. rooted
5. If you don't brush your teeth, they may have caries.
   a. decay ✓   b. enamel   c. caps
6. The lapidary was careful to not break the gems.
   a. someone who protects animals   b. someone who protects stones ✓
   c. someone who protects people

🐿 **Writing Practice:** Can you imagine yourself as a parent? What would you do if you were a parent? How would you raise your children?

©Teacher Created Materials, Inc.   195   #3302 Daily Skills Practice—Grades 4–5

Page 196

Practice 193

Math Practice: Place Value

Answer the questions.

1. Write 3,456,100 in expanded form.	2. Write 672,008 in expanded form.	3. Write 20,000 + 8,000 + 300 + 9 in standard form.
3,000,000 + 400,000 + 50,000 + 6,000 + 100	600,000 + 70,000 + 2,000 + 8	28,309

4. Write 4,000,000 + 100,000 + 20,000 + 9,000 + 80 + 1 in standard form.	5. Teresa bought a cheeseburger for $1.50, French fries for $0.50, and a soda for $0.75. How much did she pay for her meal?
4,129,081	$2.75

Language Practice: Comprehension

Answer questions about the following facts.

Facts About Fish

- All fish live in water.
- Some are catfish.
- All fish are cold-blooded.
- Most fish have scales.
- Some fish live in fresh water.
- Some fish live in salt water.

1. Is it true that all fish live in fresh water? **No**
2. Is it true that all fish have scales? **No**
3. Is it true that all catfish live in water? **Yes**
4. Is it true that catfish are cold-blooded? **Yes**

Writing Practice: Write a paragraph using the sentence starter below.

Being a part of a family means . . .

#3302 Daily Skills Practice—Grades 4–5   196   ©Teacher Created Materials, Inc.

Page 197

Practice 194

Math Practice: Number Sentences

Write a number sentence for each word problem and solve.

1. Clarence had 139 baseball cards. He gave 23 to Allen. How many cards does he have left?	2. At the dollar store, I spent $6.48. I gave the cashier a 10 dollar bill. How much money should I get back?	3. I bought a pencil for $0.25, an eraser for $0.05, and a pack of paper for $0.75. How much did I spend in all?
139 − 23 = 116 cards	$10.00 − $6.48 = $3.52	$0.25 + $0.05 + $0.75 = $1.05

4. Josiah had a pack of notebook paper with 150 sheets. He gave four friends 6 pieces of paper each. How many sheets does he have left?	5. Ramon wants to take his 375 gumballs and put them in machines. Each machine can only hold 10 gumballs. What is the greatest number of gumball machines Ramon needs?
150 − 24 = 126 sheets	375 ÷ 10 = 37 r 5 38 machines

Language Practice: Figurative Language

Finish each hyperbole.   (Answers will vary.)

1. It rained so hard _____
2. It was so hot _____
3. My cat is so lazy _____
4. It was so foggy _____
5. My little sister is so annoying _____
6. The room was so crowded _____

Writing Practice: Write a paragraph using the sentence starter below.

If there's one thing I hate, it's . . .

©Teacher Created Materials, Inc.   197   #3302 Daily Skills Practice—Grades 4–5

Page 198

Practice 195

Math Practice: Addition

Add the numbers in each column. Then solve problem 5.

1.	2.	3.
98 76 54 + 32 **260**	145 163 237 + 846 **1,391**	2,965 4,526 2,632 + 5,038 **15,161**

4.	5. Doreen went shopping and spent all of her money. Her total purchases were $87.35. How much change did she receive? What else do you need to know about this problem?
10,132 12,573 35,742 + 54,624 **113,071**	a. what she bought ⓑ how much money she gave the cashier c. you have all you need to know

Language Practice: Adverbs

Write a word before each -ly to make a sentence using adverbs. **(Answers will vary.)**

1. _____ly he sang to the baby.
2. I listened _____ly to the teacher.
3. She worked _____ly on her assignment.
4. They _____ly joined in the search for the missing wallet.
5. The band played _____ly.
6. That is a _____ly nice picture you painted.

Writing Practice: When you are feeling unhappy, what do you do? Write about how you begin to feel happy again.

#3302 Daily Skills Practice—Grades 4–5   198   ©Teacher Created Materials, Inc.

Page 199

Practice 196

Math Practice: Number Order

Solve the problems.

1. Write in order from least to greatest.	2. Write in order from least to greatest.	3. Write in order from greatest to least.
98,765 → 98.765 987.65 → 987.65 9,876.5 → 9,876.5 98.765 → 98,765	104.235 → 10.4235 10,423.5 → 104.235 1,042.35 → 1,042.35 10.4235 → 10,423.5	989 → 999 898 → 989 999 → 899 899 → 898

4. Write in order from greatest to least.	5. Noah brought 2 of most every kind of animal into the ark. If there were 189 kinds of animals, how many animals were in the ark?
2,003,005 → 2,003,005 200,300.5 → 200,300.5 20,030.05 → 20,030.05 2,003,005 → 2,003,005	378 animals

Language Practice: Interjections

Write an interjection before each sentence.   (Answers will vary.)

1. _____! Watch out for that car!
2. _____! That hurt!
3. _____! We won the game!
4. _____! I hate squash!
5. _____! The football team lost!
6. _____! I won the contest!

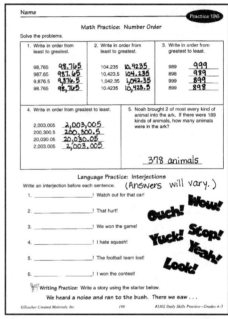

Writing Practice: Write a story using the starter below.

We heard a noise and ran to the bush. There we saw . . .

©Teacher Created Materials, Inc.   199   #3302 Daily Skills Practice—Grades 4–5

Page 200

Practice 197

Math Practice: Division

Solve each problem.

1.	2.	3.
1,115 r 3 8)8,923	9.19 5)45.95	2,070 12)24,840

4.	5. Shawn read 78 pages in the novel *The Giver*. If there are 321 pages, how many more pages does he have to read?
70,605 11)776,655	243 pages

Language Practice: Vocabulary

Match the word with the definition.

b. 1. moving air — a. air
c. 2. water falling to the earth in drops — b. wind
g. 3. study of weather — c. rain
f. 4. cloud close to the ground — d. sleet
d. 5. frozen rain — e. barometer
h. 6. sound that follows lightning — f. fog
e. 7. instrument used to measure air pressure — g. meteorology
a. 8. invisible mixture of gases surrounding the earth — h. thunder

Writing Practice: Have you ever wanted to be a famous athlete? What sport would you be famous for? Write about how you would become famous.

#3302 Daily Skills Practice—Grades 4–5   200   ©Teacher Created Materials, Inc.

Page 201

Practice 198

Math Practice: Multiplication/Decimals

Solve each problem.

1.	2.	3.
0.06 × 0.6 = 0.036	0.4 × 30.2 = 12.08	5 × 0.05 = 0.25

4.	5. 25 students were asked how often they read a book. 10 said they read at least 5 days a week. What percentage of the students read at least 5 days a week?
6.0 × 0.7 = 4.2	40%

Language Practice: Analogies

Complete each analogy.

1. Wings are to butterflies, as fins are to **fish**
2. Chimney is to house, as **peak** is to mountain.
3. Mother is to child, as cow is to **calf**
4. Pen is to chicken, as **stable** is to horse.
5. 5 is to pentagon, as 8 is to **octagon**
6. Grapes are to jelly, as apples are to **applesauce**
7. Antlers are to deer, as **horns** are to unicorns.
8. Pencils are to writing instruments, as **(Answers can vary.)** are to tools.

Writing Practice: Picture yourself 10 years from now. What do you think you'll be doing? Write about it.

©Teacher Created Materials, Inc.   201   #3302 Daily Skills Practice—Grades 4–5

Page 202

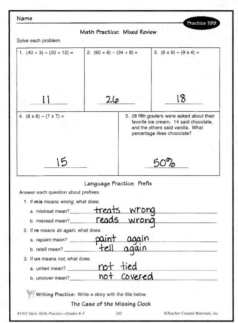

Name _____ Practice 199

Math Practice: Mixed Review

Solve each problem.

1. (40 ÷ 3) − (20 + 12) =	2. (60 ÷ 8) − (34 + 8) =	3. (6 × 9) − (9 × 4) =
11	26	18

4. (8 × 8) − (7 × 7) =	5. 28 fifth graders were asked about their favorite ice cream. 14 said chocolate, and the others said vanilla. What percentage likes chocolate?
15	50%

Language Practice: Prefix

Answer each question about prefixes.

1. If **mis** means _wrong_, what does:
   a. mistreat mean? treats wrong
   b. misread mean? reads wrong

2. If **re** means _do again_, what does:
   a. repaint mean? paint again
   b. retell mean? tell again

3. If **un** means _not_, what does:
   a. untied mean? not tied
   b. uncover mean? not covered

✍ Writing Practice: Write a story with the title below.

The Case of the Missing Clock

Page 203

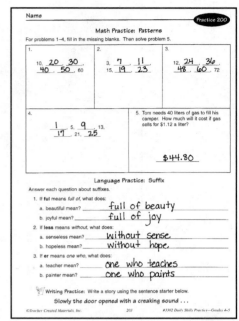

Name _____ Practice 200

Math Practice: Patterns

For problems 1–4, fill in the missing blanks. Then solve problem 5.

1.	2.	3.
10, 20, 30, 40, 50, 60	3, 7, 11, 15, 19, 23	12, 24, 36, 48, 60, 72

4.	5. Tom needs 40 liters of gas to fill his camper. How much will it cost if gas sells for $1.12 a liter?
1, 5, 9, 13, 17, 21, 25	$44.80

Language Practice: Suffix

Answer each question about suffixes.

1. If **ful** means _full of_, what does:
   a. beautiful mean? full of beauty
   b. joyful mean? full of joy

2. If **less** means _without_, what does:
   a. senseless mean? without sense
   b. hopeless mean? without hope

3. If **er** means _one who_, what does:
   a. teacher mean? one who teaches
   b. painter mean? one who paints

✍ Writing Practice: Write a story using the sentence starter below.

Slowly the door opened with a creaking sound . . .

Page 204

Name _____ Practice 201

Math Practice: Measurement

For problems 1–4, write the correct answers. Then solve problem 5.

1. At 100° C, do you take a bath or boil eggs?	2. At 0° C, do you freeze ice cream or cook hotdogs?	3. At 35° C, do you wear a bathing suit or wear a jacket?
boil eggs	freeze ice cream	wear a bathing suit

4. At 40° C, are you at the North Pole or the Sahara Desert?	5. If John was cold, and he looked at the thermometer and it said 32°, would it be Celsius or Fahrenheit?
Sahara Desert	Fahrenheit

Language Practice: Adverb/Verb

Underline the verb and circle each adverb.

1. The football player fell down.

2. The old dog just lies there.

3. The fire trucks drove nearby.

4. The pool table sits downstairs in the den.

5. The young baby crawled over to me.

6. The big dogs barked loudly.

7. The jet plane landed today.

8. My good friend arrives tomorrow.

✍ Writing Practice: Write a story using the sentence starter below.

In the year 2020 . . .

Page 205

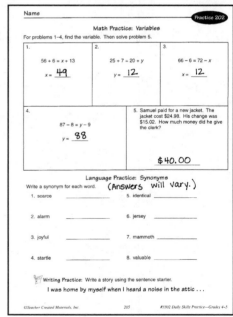

Name _____ Practice 202

Math Practice: Variables

For problems 1–4, find the variable. Then solve problem 5.

1.	2.	3.
$56 + 6 = x + 13$ $x = 49$	$25 + 7 = 20 + y$ $y = 12$	$66 − 6 = 72 − x$ $x = 12$

4.	5. Samuel paid for a new jacket. The jacket cost $24.98. His change was $15.02. How much money did he give the clerk?
$87 − 8 = y − 9$ $y = 88$	$40.00

Language Practice: Synonyms

Write a synonym for each word.   (Answers will vary.)

1. scarce _____   5. identical _____

2. alarm _____   6. jersey _____

3. joyful _____   7. mammoth _____

4. startle _____   8. valuable _____

✍ Writing Practice: Write a story using the sentence starter.

I was home by myself when I heard a noise in the attic . . .